A Tapestry of Tales

Published in 1993 by CollinsEducational,
77-85 Fulham Palace Road, London W6 8JB
An imprint of HarperCollins*Publishers*

Reprinted 1994 (twice)

© HarperCollins*Publishers* 1993

ISBN 0 00 312000 7

Series planned by Lucy Hall
Edited by Paula Hammond
Design and artwork by Derek Lee

Text set in Palatino by Derek Lee
Linotronic output by Dorchester Typesetting Group Ltd
Printed in Great Britain by Scotprint Ltd, Musselburgh.

Religion, Education And Life

A Tapestry of Tales

Elizabeth Breuilly and Sandra Palmer

Collins Educational

An imprint of HarperCollins*Publishers*

Contents

Indicates stories which are more suitable for older children.

Tales from the Buddhists

Tales from Christianity

Tales from the Hindus

Tales from Islam

Tales from Judaism

Tales from the Sikhs

Tales of Money and Other Riches

Tales of the Wise and the Foolish

Tales of Life, Death and the Underworld

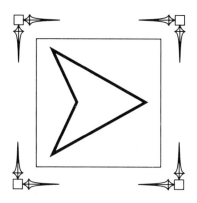

Introduction

Stories have a time honoured place in religion. Each new generation learns the significance of important events in their faith's history by hearing the tales told and retold from an early age. Stories about the lives of important people in a faith can make them seem more real and offer examples to emulate. Stories can also explore values and express fundamental religious concepts such as hope, redemption and love. They can address questions of meaning such as, "Why are things as they are?". Above all, stories can stir in adults and children a sense of the spiritual and the mysterious (in the religious sense of the word).

In religious education the traditional stories of faiths have a double function. They can deepen the children's understanding of a particular religion by helping them begin to grasp what a person or event means to its followers. They are also a way in which children can explore moral problems and experience emotional suffering (albeit at a sub-conscious level) without it being threatening.

The stories in this volume reflect this double function. All the traditional stories referred to in the REAL teacher's handbooks and assembly books are included here. These are supplemented by tales from the six major religions (Buddhism, Christianity, Hinduism, Islam, Judaism, and Sikhism) which are covered by the

REAL scheme, as well as stories from ancient civilisations and cultures. Notes referring back to specific story-related work in the handbooks or assembly books, or to the source of further information on a story-related topic, can be found at the end of the tales.

The stories included in this book come from both oral and written traditions. Some may already be familiar to both you and the children. However, because many of the stories come from a primarily oral tradition with no fixed written form don't be surprised if a child says that the story wasn't quite like that when they heard it at home, or even that they know a radically different story. (For example, many traditions have more than one account of how the world was made.) Some stories, while having an oral history behind them, have become part of the sacred texts and these have been the main source for the versions here.

Many of these stories are clearly entirely legendary. Others have an historical basis, although the extent of their historical truth may be a matter of dispute – especially when the stories concern a major figure or event in a faith. It is important to remember, however, that there will probably be many children who believe in the literal historical truth of the stories which belong to their faith, even though non-believers may view them more sceptically. Therefore there can be no *definitive* answer to the often asked question: "But did it really happen, is it true?". Only an honest response can be given by the teacher, acknowledging that there is a variety of opinion on the matter. In the primary years general discussions about fiction can help develop an awareness that stories may express truths without being historically accurate.

Sometimes children may give their own quirky interpretations to the surface meaning of religious stories, causing amusement to some adults and dismay to others. It is only to be expected that children, like all of us, will interact with a story in the light of their own knowledge and experience. As the children grow in maturity and experience the meaning the story has for them will change ≈ especially if they are given the opportunity to return and reflect on it again. It is important, then, that teachers do not impose their own interpretation of a story's "hidden meaning" on the children, but allow the story to speak for itself.

Many of these stories lend themselves to dramatization and

illustration in the classroom. These can be effective ways for the children to become emotionally engaged with the stories. Indeed most of the stories have long histories of being told in such a way. The exception is the Islamic faith, because the portrayal of the human form, especially Muhammad, is forbidden. Depicting God is strictly prohibited in both Islam and Judaism.

There are stories in the two assembly books which could well be used in the classroom, just as there are stories in this volume which could be used in assemblies. They are listed in the assembly books and cross-referenced, where appropriate, in the notes which appear at the end of the tales.

These stories have been written as a resource for the whole of the Primary years. Not all of these stories, however, will be suitable for every class. They vary in difficulty, and the class's background will make a difference. The stories which you may find suitable for older children are clearly indicated on the contents pages, and many of the tales can easily be adapted to suit the listening capabilities of younger children.

We offer these stories to you in the expectation that as you read them through to select them you will enjoy them and that subsequently you will enjoy sharing them with your class.

Acknowledgements

Many people have helped in the preparation of these stories, so if we have forgotten to mention some we apologise. Many of the stories have been told and retold, edited and re-edited by several hands. We thank in particular Vida Barnett who gave us many of the creation stories and others, Martin Palmer who told us several of the stories, Angela Smith who collected much of the material, Ranchor Prime for the stories of Krishna, Kerry Brown for "Sita in the Fire", Pastor Obed Ochwanyi for "Ahera and the Dragon" and Rev. Moses Mungai for "The Foolish Old Man". The tales "The Orphan Who Cried" and "The Widow's Children" are adapted from the anthology *Australia Dreaming* – by Jennifer Isaacs. "Olorun and Orishanla" first appeared in *Worlds of Difference*, 2nd edition, by Martin Palmer and Esther Bissett (Blackie/WWF, 1989).

Tales of How Things Began

Old One and the Five Daughters

A native Canadian creation story

Long, long, ago the world was one large sea. Above it were the clouds, and in the clouds lived Old One, Chief of the Universe. From his home in the clouds Old One would often look over the edge of the clouds and study his reflection in the waters below. Sometimes he would make up songs and dances. Sometimes he would go for long walks among the clouds. But mostly he felt bored, and very lonely.

So one day Old One decided he would make a world full of interesting creatures. He plucked five hairs from his beard, planted them in a cloud and sprinkled them with sea water. Each day he watched and tended them and they grew, and grew, and grew into five beautiful daughters with soft brown faces, twinkling eyes and long dark hair.

Then one day, Old One turned to First Daughter, and took her by the hand. "What would you most like to be?" he asked.

"I would like to be Earth, and have many children; plants, flowers and animals."

"Your wish is granted. You will cradle the growing seeds and give food and shelter to all creatures, and when they die you will again cradle them in your arms for ever."

Then Old One took Second Daughter by the hand. "What would you most like to be?" he asked.

"I would like to be Water, chuckling and laughing across the earth. I would like to have many children; water plants, water animals, fish."

"Your wish is granted. Every plant and animal on earth will drink from you and live."

Then Old One took Third Daughter by the hand. "What would you most like to be?" he asked.

"I would like to be Fire, full of light and heat. I would like to have children; lizards, snakes, insects, salamanders."

"Your wish is granted. You will bring light and warmth to all earth's creatures."

The three sisters joined hands and jumped from the clouds into the sea. As Earth plunged into the sea she changed into plains and hills and forests, filled with trees and shrubs and flowers and myriads of animals, great and small: donkeys and crocodiles and hippopotamuses and tiny shrews. Water made a great splash and the flying droplets fell on the earth as rivers and ponds and lakes. Wherever she swam water snails and oysters and rainbow fish and seals and dolphins and whales sprang into life. Fire buried herself deep in the earth, creating raging fires and volcanoes. Large sparks from the volcanoes became the sun, the moon and stars and smaller sparks lay hidden in twigs and dried leaves, waiting to be discovered.

Then Old One took his Fourth Daughter by the hand. "What would you most like to be?" he asked.

"I too would like many children, men and women. They will be happy and kind and wise. They will care for each other and share their gifts with each other and with all other creatures."

Fifth Daughter laughed: "I too will have men and women children. They will be strong and cunning and ambitious and gain power. They will know how to rule. They will rule all creatures of the world and use them for their power and glory."

Old One sighed, "Your wishes are granted. You will each give birth to children and Earth and Fire and Water will help them grow. Some will be good people, bringing happiness and joy. Others will be bad people, bringing misery and sorrow."

Then he grew thoughtful. "I had six gifts to give and so there is one gift left. I will give that gift to all men and women. It is the gift of Hope. One day good will triumph on the Earth and misery and sorrow will disappear from the world for ever."

He watched Fourth and Fifth Daughters descend to the earth and turned and walked away, never to be seen again.

The First Word

In the Hindu tradition there are many different stories about how the world and the universe were made. Here is one of them.

In the beginning there was only darkness and emptiness, but the darkness and emptiness were not cold or lifeless. There was a warmth and a dampness and a soft breathing. Gradually the breathing became a whisper and the whisper grew and grew until it filled all the space. The first word was created, "Om".

The first word had power. It created a deep ocean, and in the depths of the ocean lay a seed. Long, long years passed and the seed floated to the surface and became a huge golden egg. Gently the waves rocked it, and the light from within reached out to light up the world.

The years passed and everywhere was heard the sacred word "Om". It nourished the life within the shell and created Brahma, himself Creator of Worlds. One day the egg broke open with a loud crack. Brahma was born. From one half of the shell he created the sky; from the other he created the earth, and to keep them apart he created air.

Then Brahma created from himself many senses such as thought, hearing, sight, touch, taste, smell. He blended them together in different mixtures, creating living beings of every kind. To each kind he gave gifts. To the plants he gave two gifts: touch and the power to remake themselves with seeds and fruits. To the birds, animals and fish, he gave seven gifts: touch, taste, hearing, sight, smell and the power to remake themselves and the power of movement.

The earth teemed with the joy of new life, but one gift Brahma had not given to his creatures – the gift of thought. Many ages passed, Brahma roamed the worlds, sometimes riding a swan or a peacock, sometimes sailing the seas and the rivers in a lotus boat.

Then Brahma created from within himself another being, Sarasvati. She was beautiful. Brahma loved her and married her and they gave birth to Mani, the first human being. To him Brahma gave all of his gifts: the five senses, the power of movement, the power to remake himself and the greatest gift of all – the gift of thought.

Kang and the Great Tree

A story from the Bushmen of Southern Africa

L ong, long, ago all the people and animals lived under the earth with Kang, the creator, lord of life, and ruler of all. There was light to see by, and no one was ever hungry or sick and no one ever died.

Then, one day, Kang decided to bring the earth and sky to life. He caused a great tree to grow out of the earth, its many spreading branches creating a wondrous shade. Then he made a deep hole appear near its roots – a hole leading down to the underworld where he and all the animals and the people lived.

As the first man of all men climbed out of the hole he stared in amazement at the blue sky, the white clouds and the sunlight coming through the branches of the tree. Soon he was joined by the first woman of all women, and then more and more men and women climbed from the hole and sat down under the great tree and they too marvelled.

Kang helped the animals up through the hole, two by two, three by three, four by four, faster and faster until they came tumbling and pushing out of the earth. Some were pushed right up the tree trunk and out into the branches of the tree, only to tumble to the ground – but no one was hurt. They joined all the people sitting under the tree, and the first animals and the first people talked and talked as friends talk, all understanding the other's language. The dogs understood the lions, the birds understood the giraffes, and the people understood the insects as they hummed and buzzed.

Then Kang spoke to them. "Be happy, care for each other", he said. "There is only one thing that men and women must not do. You must never make a fire."

Kang then made the sun move across the sky each day, and hide under the earth for a while each night. But as the summer turned to autumn and autumn turned to winter, so the days grew shorter and the nights grew longer. On the longest night of all nights, the people were confused and frightened by the darkness. The air grew cool. The animals huddled together in their warm coats, but the people shivered and were afraid.

"Let us build a fire for warmth and light", called one man.

The first man of all men forgot Kang's warning. He rubbed two sticks together. They grew hot and a red glow appeared. He added leaves and twigs and soon flames lit up the darkness and the people could see and were warm. They were happy but the animals remembered Kang's warning and became afraid. They saw how the sparks flew, and they saw how the fire consumed the branches that the people put on it. The animals fled to the forest in the hills – never to return to the great tree to talk with people.

To this day people and animals can no longer understand each other because of the disobedience of the people.

⟶◆□◀⟵

11/99

The Making of Human

A native American story

In the beginning of time only animals lived on the earth. Then one day the Great Spirit asked Coyote to make a new animal which would be called Human. So Coyote called a meeting of all the animals to help him decide what Human should be like.

"Now," said Coyote, "what should this new animal be like?"

Lion spoke, "Human should have a great roar like me to frighten its enemies; fur like mine to keep it warm, and strong fangs to hunt with."

"Nonsense!" said Bear. "A being like that would have no friends. Human should be strong like me, and able to stand on its hind legs."

"No! No!" said Deer. "Human should have keen ears and sharp eyes like mine, and be able to run fast. Human should have a lightweight coat so that it will be comfortable in both hot weather and cold."

The screech of the Beaver interrupted them. "What about a tail? How can Human pick up mud and sticks and build a house without a tail?"

Very soon all the animals began to shout at one another so that Coyote became angry. "Do not be so stupid! Each of you is describing yourself and then calling yourself Human. Human must be quite different from all of us. This new creature may have certain things in common with many of us, but it must be better than all of us. Human must stand on two feet. The other two feet must be used to pick things up with. Keen eyes and ears will be necessary, but not a tail or heavy fur which will get dirty and be too hot in summer. I want Human to have soft skin like a fish, and to be clever like me, of course."

The eagle objected. "Human would not be happy without wings!"

Objections continued to come from all the animals and soon the quarrels led to fighting. Suddenly they realised that Coyote was ignoring them all. He had taken a lump of clay from the earth and was trying to shape a human. The animals grew quiet. Then each too began to make a model of the creature they wished to invent. Darkness came. They worked on and on, but gradually one and then another began to yawn. Their eyes closed and, one by one, they fell asleep.

When he was sure that everyone was asleep Coyote filled a pot with water and crept round the clearing, pouring water over all the other models until they were shapeless lumps of mud. Then he returned to his own model and finished it.

When the other animals awoke they were very angry, but before they could make new models, Coyote gave Human life. And so it is that Human has two legs to stand on, has no fur, and is much cleverer than any other creature.

Light Comes to the World

A native American story

Long, long, ago the whole world was dark. So dark that the animals could scarcely see to find food, and they grew very thin.

One day Eagle came to visit Coyote. "I wish I could offer you food," Coyote exclaimed, "but I have nothing, even for myself."

"Let us help each other", said Eagle. "Tomorrow we will go hunting together."

The next day they travelled across the plains and through the fields. Eagle swooped down upon some smaller animals but Coyote caught nothing. After sharing his food with Coyote, Eagle became very cross.

"You catch nothing, and when I give you food you leave the bones scattered over the ground."

"I know," said Coyote, "but I can't even see to bury them. We need light."

Eagle thought and thought. "I have heard that far away in the woods of the west there are two great lights; one called Sun and one called Moon. Let us try to find them and capture them", he said.

For many days they travelled. Coyote constantly bumped into things or fell into holes. Eagle grew more and more impatient with him. But after a while Coyote realised that he was not bumping into things so much. How could that be? He stopped in amazement. He could just see the outline of trees and bushes and streams and hills. The light increased. Coyote began to shout and dance with glee.

"Quiet!" shouted Eagle. He led Coyote to the top of a small hill. Below, in a grove of trees, a number of strangely coloured spirits danced and sang. Coyote's teeth chattered with fear.

"Do not be afraid", said Eagle. "They haven't seen us. Now, do you see those two great chests at the edge of the clearing? Watch."

As Coyote watched, the dancers rushed to one of the chests and lifted the lid for a moment. A shaft of light burst forth. This happened again and again. One or two of the dancers would leave the circle and rush to lift the lid of one of the chests.

"What is in the chests?" asked Coyote.

"In one is hidden Sun and in the other is Moon", replied Eagle. "Tonight, when the spirits are sleeping, we will steal them."

At last the dancers fell into an exhausted sleep. Eagle flew up high into the sky and, dropping like a stone, seized the two chests in his talons and flew rapidly away. Coyote ran after him and as he struggled on, frantically trying to keep up, he began to wonder, "What are they like, Sun and Moon? Are they very beautiful?". He begged and pleaded to be allowed to carry the chests until finally Eagle placed them on the top of the mountain and soared into the air. Coyote put a paw under the lid of the larger chest and gently raised it. A beautiful, warm light enfolded him.

"I will warm my hands!" he cried, and he stuck his paws into the chest.

"Oh!" he cried. "I'm burning!", and staggering back he threw open the lid and Sun leapt out and in one bound reached the sky.

Coyote was terrified. "I must send Moon to fetch him back." He opened the other chest and let Moon out, but no matter how hard Moon tried he could not catch Sun.

When Eagle returned and saw what had happened he was very angry. "We could have had eternal light. But now, day and night will chase each other for ever."

How Medicine was Discovered

A native American story

For many years people and animals lived peaceably on the American Prairies. The braves killed animals only when food was necessary, and the animals died willingly – proud to be of service. But as the years passed some of the braves became greedy. They killed and killed, selling the animals' flesh and fur to strangers. Slowly beavers, otters, stags and bison began to disappear from the forests and streams.

In desperation White Bear called all the animals to a meeting.

"How can we punish the humans for their cruelty and selfishness?" he said.

First of all the animals decided to make bows and arrows and fight back, but their paws and claws and hooves were clumsy against the bow strings and many more were killed. Then the birds suggested stealing all the wigwams so that the humans might die of cold. The beaver vowed to gnaw holes in the bottom of all the canoes.

Finally the oldest and wisest among all creatures, the fly, stepped forward.

"Ask the Great Spirit to send down sickness", he buzzed. "We, the flies, will take that sickness to all of the humans who have harmed us."

The animals agreed and returned to their homes. Before long sickness came to the Indian villages. It brought pain and sorrow to those who had massacred the animals. But not only to them: all men, women and children became ill, including those who had been kind to the animals. They lay in their wigwams unable to hunt and so they died. Then the animals grew sad. Their friends, as well as their enemies were dying. What could they do?

The answer came from the flowers. "Many of us have healing powers. Collect our leaves and flowers, grind and mix them to-gether and give them to the people."

The people who could walk or crawl came out of their wigwams and collected all kinds of herbs hoping to be cured. And when they did not know which herbs to use, the spirits hidden within the flow-ers whispered to them so that all might be healed. And so it was that the people of the prairies learnt how to use plants for healing.

The Monkey Who Made a Flood

A Caribbean folk tale

In the very old and far off times, all the animals and Man were friendly and helped each other. The jaguar did not attack Man, and Man did not hunt the wild animals. But Monkey was very foolish and was always playing tricks on the other animals. He pinched them and teased them and made it difficult for them to do their work.

One morning, when Man visited the stump of the Great Tree in the forest, he found a spring flowing from its roots. It did not flow smoothly and quietly like most rivers, but bubbled up strongly and urgently as though it had important work to do.

"Why are you rushing and gushing like this?" said Man to the stream.

"I must hurry, as I have to cover the whole earth before tomorrow morning", gurgled the stream.

Man realised that everyone was in danger if the stream did as it said, so he quickly gathered reeds and wove a basket. He put this over the spring, and it immediately died down and stopped flowing.

But Monkey had been watching in the forest. He saw Man make the basket and carefully place it on the ground, but he was too far away to hear what had been said.

"Aha!" he said to himself. "I've caught Man out. He's being selfish. He says he cares about us animals, but he doesn't. He is hiding the best fruit under that basket. I'll go and get some of it."

So when Man had gone, Monkey crept down and lifted the basket. At once the stream spurted out, all the more fiercely for having been held back. The great torrent swept Monkey away, and began to fill the earth. The other animals heard Monkey's terrified cry, and rushed to Man shouting, "Save us, save us!"

Quickly Man led the way up a steep hill, where coconut trees grew. All the animals and Man climbed the trees to escape from the water as it covered the whole earth.

For five days they sat in the coconut trees, eating the fruit and drinking the coconut milk, while the flood rose and a storm raged all about them.

At last the thunder and lightning ceased and the rain stopped falling. Man and the animals sat in the trees listening to the silence. Thick mist covered the whole earth, so they could not see whether the water had drained away from the earth beneath them.

Man took a coconut and dropped it out of the tree. All the animals held their breath, waiting to hear it fall. They heard a splash quite close by – the water was still high.

Next day Man did the same, and the next day, and each time the splash sounded a little further away.

After three days, instead of a splash, there was a dull thud. The water had drained away. Man told the others to wait in the tree while he went to find out if the earth was fit to stand on. When he reported that the water had indeed gone, the animals came down out of the trees. But what a miserable place the earth was! It was cold and wet, and all the animals shivered. Even Pig, who loved mud, found it was too wet for him, and searched frantically for a dry place to lie down.

Eventually Man decided to make a fire, and invited all the animals to sit beside it. But because of the monkey's foolishness which had caused the flood, the animals no longer trusted each other. From that time man only talks to man, pig only talks to pig, and Monkey only talks to monkey. They can no longer understand each other.

Olorun and Orishanla

The creation story of the Yoruba people of Nigeria

In the beginning there was no dry land, only water and marshes. Above was the sky, where Olorun, the highest god, lived with the other gods, the Orisha. At night they used to descend into the marshes and play there, swinging on the great spiders' webs which hung between earth and sky.

After a while Olorun decided to make dry land, so he summoned Orishanla, who was one of the Orisha, and gave him a snail-shell full of earth, and a five-toed hen, and said to him: "Go and make a firm place to walk on."

Orishanla threw the earth on the water below, then put down the hen. The hen began to scratch the earth this way and that way, spreading it out until it had made a large area of dry land.

Orishanla thought to himself: "Is this land good enough? How can I test it?"

"Ah!" he said to himself. "The chameleon always treads slowly and carefully on the earth. I'll ask him to test the ground for me."

Orishanla said to the chameleon: "Go. Walk on the land which I have made. Tell me, is it good?"

The chameleon obeyed Orishanla. He walked to and fro on the new land.

"It is fine and wide," he told Orishanla, "but it is not dry enough."

So Orishanla put the hen down again and it scratched some more. Again the chameleon inspected the earth, and this time he said, "It is both wide and dry. It is good."

So Orishanla returned to Olorun. "I have made dry land, and the chameleon says it is good."

"Now," said Olorun, "I have another task for you. Sow trees and plants on the earth that you have made."

Orishanla sowed trees and plants. He sowed grass and forest trees for the animals. He sowed plants which are useful to people. All this took five days.

Then Olorun decided to make people to live on the earth, so he told Orishanla, "Take some clay and make bodies of men and women."

Orishanla took some clay and made the bodies of men and women.

"But they have no life", he said.

"Leave that to me", replied Olorun. "I will give them life."

Each day Orishanla made the bodies out of clay. Each night Olorun gave them life. But Orishanla was jealous, and wanted to find out how Olorun put life into the bodies. One night he hid to see what Olorun would do with the bodies. But Olorun knew he was there watching, and put Orishanla into a deep sleep. When he woke up, the people had come alive. So he never ever found out how to bring bodies to life. Each day he goes on moulding the bodies out of clay, and each night Olorun goes on giving them life.

How does he do it? No one has ever found out.

Prometheus

A story from Ancient Greece

Long ago, in the days when there were no human beings, giant gods called Titans battled with the new gods to decide who would rule the world. The Titans were eventually defeated and punished, except for the Titan Prometheus who remained a friend of the new gods because he had wisely stayed out of the battle.

Prometheus often visited the new gods in their home on Mount Olympus, but eventually he got tired of their endless quarrelling. He went off on his own and dug up a great lump of clay from the earth. Then he wet it with river water and shaped clay figures out of it. His friend Athene, the goddess of knowledge, came down and breathed on the figures, filling them with life and soul. These were the first human beings.

Prometheus loved the humans. They were his creations, and he was even prepared to trick Zeus, the ruler of the gods, in order to help them. One day he was asked to solve an argument between the gods and humans over how sacrificial bulls should be shared out between them. To settle the matter once and for all, Prometheus cut up a bull and divided the parts into two bags. In one, he put all the bones, hidden under a gleaming layer of fat. In the other he put the tasty flesh, wrapped in the tough skin. Zeus had first choice and he greedily chose the bag with the fat on top. But when he lifted the fat and found a useless bag of bones underneath he was speechless with rage. From that time on, he did not speak to Prometheus.

Prometheus took care of the humans and taught them all the arts and sciences he learnt from Athene. He taught them how to make tools and clothing, how to build houses, how to read the stars and sail the seas, and which herbs and plants to use as medicine.

But every day the people looked with dread to the sky as the chariot of Apollo, the sun god, disappeared below the horizon.

Then the people had to sit shivering in the cold and dark as they ate a dinner of raw meat. There was still one thing missing in their lives – fire.

Prometheus decided to go and ask Zeus if he could take a flame from the sun chariot down to Earth. But when Prometheus showed his face at Mount Olympus seeking more favours for human beings, Zeus was furious. Prometheus began to tell Zeus about how miserable his people were without fire, but Zeus interrupted him.

"Your people are happy enough to keep the flesh of every bull they sacrifice! And who tricked me into letting them have it? You did! They have the flesh of their sacrificial bulls, but they will never have fire to cook it!" he bellowed.

Prometheus knew there was no arguing with him so he left at once. But he could not bear to see the people chewing miserably on raw meat, their hands blue with cold. So one evening, as the shadows grew long on the earth, he crept to the gateway of Mount Olympus. In his hands he carried a long hollow stalk and a piece of coal.

As the sun chariot galloped toward the gateway, Prometheus hid himself behind the gatepost. Then, as the chariot thundered past, he put out the hand that was holding the piece of coal and caught a spark of fire from the chariot's wheel. He dropped the burning coal into the hollow stalk so its light was hidden from sight. Then, under cover of dark, Prometheus ran down the mountain, back to the land of the humans with his precious gift.

For a while all was well. Then, one night as Zeus was walking on the wall of Mount Olympus in the cool of the evening he glanced down at the earth and saw in the darkness a thousand twinkling lights. When he realised these were not stars but a thousand fires, Zeus knew at once that it must be the work of Prometheus.

He let out a mighty roar. Furious at being outwitted by Prometheus once more, he ordered his two strongest messengers to find Prometheus so he could be given a punishment that would last for eternity.

Prometheus was found and taken to the last great rocky mountain at the eastern edge of the world. There he was chained to its peak so the bitter winds from beyond the world's edge whistled through his bones, and the blistering sun beat down upon his naked skin. But worst of all was the huge eagle that came every day to devour his liver. Because Prometheus was immortal, his liver grew back each night so the next day he suffered again the terrible pain when the eagle returned to tear at him with its talons and beak.

Only one thing could have won Zeus' forgiveness. Zeus had been warned that one day he would be overthrown as ruler of the gods. Prometheus could see many things in the future and knew how this would happen, but he refused to gain Zeus' pardon by telling him. So for thousands of years Prometheus was tortured for giving fire to humanity.

Feb 07

Demeter and Persephone

A story from Ancient Greece

Demeter was the goddess of the earth. It was she who caused crops to grow; she who made the harvest ripe in the fields; she who made fruit grow sweet and heavy on the branches; she who had first taught men and women how to plant seeds, and care for the young shoots.

Demeter had one child, a daughter Persephone, whom she dearly loved, and who was nearly an adult.

Now one day Persephone was out in the fields with her friends gathering flowers – laughing and singing together as they filled their baskets to overflowing with violets and lilies. The day was light and sunny, and happiness seemed to surround them.

Suddenly their peace was shattered. Charging towards them came two huge powerful horses pulling the chariot of Hades, the god of the underworld. The girls shrank back frightened by the mighty beasts but, as his carriage swept past, Hades saw Persephone and was immediately smitten by her beauty. So instant and violent were his feelings for her that he leaned over and caught her by the waist, pulling her screaming with him.

Persephone cried out in terror: "Mother! Mother!"

Hades took no notice of her desperate cries, but urged his horses on faster and faster through rivers and lakes, over mountains and down valleys.

The nymph Cyane heard Persphone's screams and rose out of her watery home to try and stop Hades. "You will go no further", she said. "You must return Persephone to her mother. You should have wooed the girl, not seized her against her will."

Hades was furious that anyone should try to stop him taking Persephone away. He pushed the nymph out of his way and, taking his royal sceptre, struck the bottom of the pool. The ground beneath opened up and the horses and chariot plunged into the fearsome darkness of the underworld, taking the wailing Persephone with them.

Cyane, in her grief for the girl, melted into the pool becoming one with the water. On the water's surface floated Persephone's sash. She had flung it out in a last attempt to leave a sign behind her.

Meanwhile Demeter was frantically searching for her daughter. All through the earth she wandered, calling her name, seeking just one person who could tell her where her daughter had gone. At last she came across the sash. Recognizing it, she rescued it from the water and held it to her tightly.

For the first time her anger and grief came pouring forth. She cursed the world for not protecting her child. The earth she had nurtured for so long now bore her fury. She broke the ploughs, she caused weeds and thistles to choke the crops, she sent plague and famine.

But her anger did not bring her back her lost child, and her quest continued until she came to the river Arethusa. The goddess of the river rose up and spoke to Demeter: "The earth does not deserve your wrath. Your daughter has been taken to the underworld. On my journeys from the mountains to the sea I descend for a time to travel through the underworld before emerging again. There in the underworld I have seen Persephone. She looks pale and sad, but you should comfort yourself for Hades has made her his queen."

Demeter was not comforted. She stormed to Mount Olympus and the palace of Zeus, ruler of all the gods, and demanded that her daughter be returned to her.

Zeus looked at the distraught mother. He looked at the tormented earth beneath him and he heard the prayers of the suffering people. He pronounced his judgement. Yes, Persephone could return to the upper world, but on one condition – that she had not eaten anything in the world below. If she had she would belong to that world.

But Persephone had eaten, just once in all her long stay. Absent-mindedly she had plucked a pomegranate from one of the trees when she had ben walking sorrowfully in Hades' gardens. She had eaten seven pomegranate seeds.

Demeter claimed that, because Persephone had eaten so little during her time in the underworld, she should be allowed to return to earth with her. However Hades claimed that because she had eaten even such a small amount she must stay with him in the underworld.

Eventually Zeus decided that for six months of the year Persephone would stay with her mother, but for the other six months she must return to her husband in the underworld.

And so it is that when Persephone is with her mother the world is full of light and growth – it is green and fresh. But for the other six months, when she must live with Hades, the world is cold and barren – for Demeter is mourning the loss of her daughter. This is one story of why we have the seasons.

Note:
This story can be told in conjunction with work on 'The living world' in the *Junior Teacher's Handbook*, page 9.

Adam Names the Animals

The Talmud is a great collection of Jewish wisdom: arguments and judgements by rabbis, explanations and discussions of the Torah – the Jewish holy book – and traditional tales which help Jews to understand God's teachings. The following two stories are re-told from the Talmud.

I n the beginning, God created the heavens and the earth, the seas and fishes, the air and the birds, the land and the animals. But none of these creatures had names. Last of all, God created Adam and his wife Eve. All the other creatures had sprung forth from the earth or the sea by God's command, but Adam and Eve he moulded with his own hands.

Now Adam was perfect when he was created: perfectly formed, strong, handsome and wise. Adam was even wiser than the angels. When he was only an hour old (but not a child, for he was created as a grown man), God assembled all the creatures he had made. They came before God and his angels, and God told his angels to give them all their proper name. There were large beasts and small beasts, the lion and the elephant, the mouse and the kangaroo; there were all the birds of the air, from the eagle to the tiny humming-bird; there were the insects and spiders and brilliantly coloured butterflies; and there were the fish of the sea, the shark, the herring and the tiny plankton that live in the sea but no one can see.

The angels began the task of giving each creature its proper name, but they found they could not manage it. They looked at the myriad creatures that God in his wisdom and power had created, and they could not find the right name for each one. But Adam spoke up without hesitation: "O Lord of all the world, King of the Universe, the proper name for this animal is lion, for this one elephant, for this one mouse, for this one dolphin, for this one crab, for this one mosquito..." and so on, until he had given each creature its name. And all the names he gave to all the creatures were exactly suited to their nature, and to the particular skill that God had given them. Nowadays we have forgotten what many of the names mean, but Adam knew, and God was pleased with his naming.

Then God said to Adam, "And what is your name?" And Adam answered, "My name is Adam, because you made me out of the dust of the earth, which is called Adamah."

And God said to Adam, "And what is my name?"

And Adam replied, "You are Adonai, the Lord, because you are Lord over all that you have created; the earth, the heavens, the sea, the sky, over all the creatures, and over me and my wife."

God replied, "Yes! You are right. The Lord is my name for ever and ever."

Note:
This story can be told in conjunction with work on 'Pets' in the *Infant Teacher's Handbook*, page 45

Adam and Eve Learn to Make Fire

Jews believe that God created our world, but that he created people to enjoy and use the world for the benefit of every living thing. They believe that when people take the things that God has created to make new things for the benefit of all of humankind they become partners with God in creation. Jewish children remember this when they hear the story of how Adam and Eve built the first fire.

A dam and Eve had had a wonderful first day on earth in the Garden of Eden; naming the animals, smelling the flowers, marvelling at the greenness of the grass and the trees. They listened to the running water and the wind rustling the leaves, but most of all they enjoyed the warmth of the sunlight.

But as the day wore on, the garden began to change. The sun's warmth began to go and coldness crept upon them. As the sun went, so did the light and soon it was impossible to see what lay around them. Strange shapes and shadows loomed up beside them and fear entered their hearts. So great was their fear that they called out to God.

"What is wrong?" asked God, concerned for the man and woman he had created.

"We are cold. It's becoming dark. What will become of us?"

"Do not be afraid. I will show you how to conquer your fear. Find me two stones which are black and hard."

It was not easy to search in the fading light but eventually Adam and Eve each found a stone.

God said: "One stone is called 'Darkness', the other is called 'Shadow of Death'. Gather some small twigs and dry grass and make a small pile of them. Then let Eve gather some larger twigs and place them near the pile."

Adam and Eve were puzzled, cold and miserable but they did what God told them to do.

"Now, Adam, hold the stones over the pile of twigs and rub them together, hard."

Adam rubbed and rubbed. At first nothing happened and he was very discouraged.

"Don't give up", God told him. "Trust in me."

Again and again Adam rubbed the stones together, and then it happened. A spark flew from the stones and a piece of dried grass began to smoulder and suddenly burst into flame. As the small twigs caught fire God told Eve to gently feed the flames with the larger branches she had gathered. Gradually the warmth of the fire surrounded them. They stopped shivering and as the light of the fire helped them see each other they were no longer afraid. They laughed and danced with joy.

"Blessed art Thou, Oh Lord, Our God, who created Light", sang Adam, using the words that Jewish families use today when they light the Sabbath candles before eating their evening meal.

Eve was curious. "Why do the stones have such strange names?" she asked. "Why 'Darkness', why 'Shadow of Death'?"

From the darkness beyond the light created by the flames, God's voice answered quietly: "Because you are made in my image, you can take the black stone of darkness and the cold stone which is the shadow of death, and create light and warmth through fire. And so in your lives you too can take darkness, and even the shadow of death, and create light, warmth and freedom from fear."

The Naming of the Years

In China the years are named after twelve different animals. This is a story of how this came to be.

The Jade King lived in heaven, and ruled the earth and the sky. He had servants to do everything for him, and all he had to do all day was to sit and give orders. One day he called his Chief Adviser. "I'm bored!" he said.

"Bored, your majesty?" said the Chief Adviser. "How can that be so?"

"I sit here all day long giving orders, and I never get to do anything or see anything interesting. Why, I've never even seen the animals that live on the earth! What do they look like?"

"Well, there are many animals on the earth, and they all look different. There is the cat who is small and furry, and the fishes who are smooth and have no legs, and the birds who are covered with feathers and can fly, and the sheep who has wool on its back, and ... "

"Stop, stop!" cried the Jade King. "This is no good! I want to see them for myself."

"Very good, your majesty", said the Chief Adviser. "Er... was your majesty wishing to see all the different animals on earth?"

"Well, how many are there?" asked the Jade King.

"Oh, I think probably about a thousand million", said the Chief Adviser.

"Oh, I see. Yes, that might be a bit much, even for me. I know! You go and choose twelve animals, and invite them to my palace, and I will put them in order of who is most interesting."

So the Chief Adviser went away and thought about which animals he should invite to the palace. In the end, this is what he decided:

He invited the rat and asked him to bring his friend the cat as well.

He invited the ox, the tiger and the rabbit.

He invited the dragon, the snake and the horse.

He invited the ram, the monkey, the cock and the dog.

The rat was very proud to be invited to go to see the Jade King, and he set off to tell his friend the cat. "We're invited to the Palace of the Jade King!" he said. "Six o'clock tomorrow morning."

"That's wonderful!" said the cat. "But – six o'clock? That's very early. I don't know if I can wake up that early. I know! You come and wake me up, and then we can go to the palace together."

"All right", said the rat. "See you tomorrow."

But when he got home, the rat began to think: "If I go to the palace with the cat, the Jade King will never notice me. The cat is such a fine looking creature, and so clever at jumping and running and purring, he is bound to be put in first place. No, I'm not going to wake him up. I'll go to the palace on my own."

So the next day there were eleven animals lined up before the Jade King.

"Well, they all look very interesting," said the king, "but why are there only eleven?"

The Chief Adviser did not know what to say. He was afraid the King would think he had not done his job properly. So he sent for one of his servants and whispered to him, "Quick! Go back to earth and bring me the first animal you see!"

The servant went to earth, and the first thing he saw was a man carrying a pig.

"It's not very interesting," thought the servant, "but it will have to do." And he took the pig back to the palace.

Then the Jade King started to judge the competition to see which animal was the most interesting. He walked up and down the line, looking at all the animals, and seeing what they could do. The rat was afraid that the king would never notice him, he was so small. So he made a plan.

As the king came by, he jumped on to the back of the ox, and began to play a flute. He whistled and he piped, and he jumped up and down, playing all the tunes he knew. The king stopped.

"Now that," he said, "is the most interesting animal I have seen all day. I give the first place to the rat!"

Then the king put all the other animals in order.

The ox got second place, because he had been kind and had let the rat sit on his back.

The tiger got third place, because he looked so fierce, and the rabbit got fourth place, because he had such beautiful fur.

The dragon got fifth place, because he looked like a snake on legs.

Then came the snake, the horse, the ram, the monkey, the cock and the dog.

Then the king looked at the pig. "It's really quite ugly," he said, "and it's not very interesting. But it's here, so I suppose I shall have to give it twelfth place."

Just as the king had announced all of the places, the cat came rushing in.

"Look at me! Look at me!" he cried to the king. He arched his back and purred, and curled his tail, and jumped as high as he could. The king was most impressed.

"Yes, you are a very interesting animal," he said, "but I'm afraid that you're too late. I have decided all the places, and the rat has come first."

When the cat heard this, he glared at the rat, and bared his teeth and stretched out his claws. He rushed at the rat and tried to catch him and kill him. But the rat was too quick and he just got away.

That is why, even today, a cat cannot be friends with a rat.

Note:
This story can be told in conjunction with work on 'Introducing Chinese New Year', in the *Infant Teacher's Handbook*, page 64.

Kuan Yin and the Peacock

A tale from Ancient China

Long, long, ago when P'an Ku ruled the earth and animals had only just begun to walk its surface, Kuan Yin, goddess of mercy, walked with them. She showed them where to build their homes, where to find shelter, and she showed them where to find their food. She talked and sang with the animals and they delighted in her company. All was peaceful in those times, for no one would quarrel while Kuan Yin was there.

But then came the day when Kuan Yin called all the animals to her. "My friends," she said, "today I am leaving you to return to my heavenly palace. I have taught you how to live on this earth and now I have other tasks to do. I will come back to visit you from time to time, but my home will no longer be with you. Farewell."

So saying she stood on the foot of the rainbow, that bridge which links earth with heaven, and glided upwards until the clouds hid her from sight.

No sooner had she gone than the animals began to quarrel.

"I will miss her", said the rabbit. "I was always her favourite you know. She took especial care when she showed me how to dig my burrow."

"What do you mean you were her favourite?" spluttered the cat. "I was her favourite. She loved to stroke my fur and have me curl up in her lap."

The horse protested. "No, no, no, it was me Kuan Yin loved the most. My graceful movement gave her great joy – she often said so."

Soon other animals joined in the argument, each claiming that they had been Kuan Yin's favourite, and before long the air was filled with the sounds of hissing and spitting, neighing and braying, squeaking and screeching as the animals fought with each other.

The noise grew stronger and stronger until the din was so great that it reached the heavens and Kuan Yin herself.

The animals were so engrossed in their quarrel that they did not notice Kuan Yin descend her rainbow bridge. It just seemed that she was suddenly in their midst. there

"My friends, my friends", she said. "What is this? Can you not live in peace with one another as you did when I was here? I love you all equally. Please promise me that you'll stop this fighting."

The animals hung their heads in shame. The snake became knotted up with his tail as he frantically tried to hide his head in embarrassment.

"We are very very sorry", they all chorused. "We will not argue again. We promise we will live in harmony."

But hardly had Kuan Yin disappeared when the bickering began again. The ox muttered under his breath: "Well at least I wasn't as much to blame as some."

"What do you mean you weren't to blame?" the others turned on him indignantly, and the whole thing started once more.

This time Kuan Yin was very, very, angry. Her face was stern and grim.

"I trusted you and you have broken your trust", she said. "What am I to do with you?"

The animals shook with fear but were silent, until eventually a little voice piped up, "We would be good, if you were here to watch over us".

"Yes!" the other animals chorused. "We would be good then, we would... we would. Please stay with us, Kuan Yin."

"But I cannot be with you all the time", said Kuan Yin. "I must help others who are in need." Then suddenly she smiled a gentle smile. "Ah! I know! I have an idea", she said, and she beckoned to a drab, dowdy bird who had had no part in the quarrelling, but had stood quivering on the edge.

"Come here my shy one", she said. "You will be my presence here on earth", Kuan Yin announced. "You will have grace and beauty, and you will have a hundred eyes to watch over these naughty children of mine when I am away." And she transformed the drab, dowdy bird into a bird of glistening blues and greens. She gave him a long tail of feathers which stood like a great fan behind him, and into the fan she set a hundred eyes to watch over the animals.

Today we call him the peacock.

Note:
This story can be told in conjunction with work on 'Chinese New Year' in the *Infant Teacher's Handbook*, page 62.

Feb '07

Creating the Animals

A tale from the Australian Aborigines

I n the far off time all beings were asleep, dreaming through the world's first long night. No people, animals, birds, grass, trees, streams, rivers were found on the earth. There was no movement, no noise. At last the Father of All Spirits awoke the Sun Mother. She looked down on the earth and was sad for she saw only a bare and empty world.

The Father of All Spirits spoke: "Go down to earth. Cover the ground with grass and trees. Fill the rivers and streams with water. Bring to life all insects and fish and reptiles and birds and animals."

The Sun Mother sped to earth and wherever her warmth touched the cold ground, grasses, trees and flowers sprang up. Soon she came to a deep, dark cave. She entered it and walked down, down into the earth. Her light and warmth wakened the insects: ants, beetles, butterflies, bees, swarmed through the opening of the cave and out into the green countryside, filling it with colour.

Deeper and deeper into the earth moved the Sun Mother. Ice melted under her feet. Snakes, lizards, frogs and tortoises stretched and crawled upwards into the light and a river, filled with fish of many kinds, rushed from the mouth of the cave. The Sun Mother moved on to wake the spirits of the birds: ducks and swans and magpies and pelicans. In yet another cave she found the koala bears, the kangaroos, the emus, the porcupines, the wild dogs. Willingly they all followed her to the surface.

Then the Sun Mother spoke to all her children: "I must return to the sky but I will always give you light and warmth. Live together in friendship. Do not seek to do any harm. Enjoy the earth until the day when your bodies fall asleep and return to dust and your spirits live on to dream unseen until they are again awakened and given new bodies."

For a while all creatures lived peacefully together. Then some became greedy and jealous. The kangaroos wanted to fly, the lizard wanted to swing from the trees, the fish wanted feet to run on the bottom of the sea. More and more they quarrelled until one day Sun Mother left the sky to talk with them.

"My children, I grieve that you are so dissatisfied. Choose what kind of living creatures you want to be. One day you may be sorry, but just for today you may have the power to change yourselves into any shape you wish."

What strange creatures emerged! Fish grew wings and appeared to fly. Possums turned into bats. Wallabies climbed trees. Insects looked like twigs. Kangaroos grew a pouch and a tail. But the Platypus became the strangest creature of all. It had a bill like a duck, it laid eggs, it had teeth to chew with and a beaver's tail. Two feet were webbed like a duck. All four feet had bear's claws and its babies suckled milk from its breast. Seeing such a strange creature Sun Mother said, "I must make a new creature. It will have more of my mind and will be superior to all the creatures."

The Sun Mother bore two beautiful children; the morning star and the morning. They in turn had two other children. Their grandmother sent them to earth. These were the first man and the first woman.

"My children", she said, "live together in peace as long as you live. You have no need to envy any other living thing and when you die your spirits will live as stars for ever."

Note:

These strange creatures all exist – there is a flying squirrel which resembles both a possum and a bat. There are tree-climbing wallabies, flying fish and stick insects.

The Rainbow Snake

A story from the Australian Aborigines

It was very, very, hot. Day after day the sun shone relentlessly down. All the trees died. There was no shade and the lakes and the rivers dried up. The people were very hungry, for all the animals had moved away to find water and the fish remained down stream. A small snake watched their fear and their sorrow and he crawled out from his resting place beneath the rock and said, "If you wish, I could help you, for I possess magic. Throw me up into the sky."

Now there was one man in the tribe who thought that only he had magical powers. He was the Shaman, and people always turned to him when they were in trouble. He scorned the snake and laughed at it. "You would only fall down and be killed", he said.

"If you obey and trust me I will hold on to the sky with my scales and I will scratch some rain and snow free from the clouds, for they are made of blue ice."

"You are too small", mocked the Shaman.

"Just throw me up as high as you can", said the snake. "Will it hurt you to try?"

The Shaman thought to himself, "Things are so bad. Perhaps I should try anything, no matter how foolish it seems."

So he bent down, picked up the snake and flung it towards the sky with all his might. As it flew upwards the snake began to uncoil.

The people watched it grow longer and longer, until its head rested on one edge of the horizon and its tail curled round the other. His spine arched upwards and scraped the sky. They marvelled as the snake's body constantly changed colour: red, yellow, green, purple. The ice in the sky melted. The healing rain came pouring down upon the earth. The water filled up the dry river beds. The grass began to grow. The trees bore fruit. Animals came back to graze and the fish again swam up the river. The people danced with joy, thanking and honouring the snake. And to this day whenever there is rain on a sunny day, you can see the snake arching its body across the sky.

The Widow's Children

A story from the Australian Aborigines of New South Wales

Baiame, the great ancestor, had called a meeting of all the people of his tribe. The season was good, with plenty of food in the bush for the women to gather as they travelled to the meeting, plenty of water in the water-holes, and plenty of animals for the men to hunt. So the people travelled easily and fast, family group joining with family group, as they all came nearer to the place where the meeting was.

When they reached the meeting place, they held a ceremony for some of the boys who were old enough to be treated as men and join the hunting parties. The old men took the boys away to a secret place, and the rest of the tribe camped for the night where they were. The next morning they were all going to move on to another meeting place for the rest of the ceremony.

But just as they were about to set off, into the camp staggered the widow Millindoo, thin, weary, and covered in mud.

"You left me!" she cried. "You all travelled as fast as you could, with never a thought for me and my five children! You know the little ones can't keep up! Did you think I had more than one back and more than two feet? How could I carry so many children? Not one of you stayed to help me. You didn't even give me a thought! You drank all the water from the water holes as you passed. Every time we struggled to a water hole, and my children lay down exhausted, and cried for water, what did I find? Mud, nothing but mud! My children cried and fainted, and I, their mother could do nothing! Do you know what it is like for a mother to see her children cry for water, and have none to give them? One by one, my children lay down in the dust and died."

At this the tribe were struck with remorse for their selfish behaviour. One of the women quickly picked up a pot of water, and went to give it to the widow.

"Too late!" cried Millindoo. "My children are dead, why should I live now? I needed this water yesterday, not today!"

But as the cool, refreshing water touched her swollen tongue and her dry, rasping throat, she roused herself for one last effort. Drawing herself up from the ground, she stood and looked at the tribes gathered round. She waved her hands at them, and shouted, "You were in such a hurry to get here, now you can stay here for ever!" And with that she fell back on the ground and died.

And at once the tribes standing nearest her were changed into trees. Those a little further back were changed into animals or birds, each according to the name they were known by. The pigeon tribe were changed into pigeons, the dog tribe into dogs, the pelican tribe into pelicans, and so on.

And to this very day, on that spot, you can see the trees waving their branches and sighing and wailing, as the animals and birds gather for their meeting by the waters.

The Orphan Who Cried

A story from the Australian Aborigines

There was once a boy in the Gunwinggu tribe whose mother and father were both dead. He did not go short of anything, for his aunts and his uncles and his older cousins and his big brothers and sisters all made sure that he had plenty of food, and took care of him. But this orphan would not stop crying.

The trouble was that he had once tasted lily roots. These were a special sort of lily roots that the women searched for with their toes in the black mud by the rivers, and then boiled for everyone to eat. There are several kinds of lily root in Australia that are good to eat, but this special sort was delicious. And once the orphan had tasted these, he would not eat anything else. All he did was cry and cry for lily roots.

One day when he was walking around crying, he met an old lady.

"Why are you crying, little boy?" she asked.

"They won't give me any of the special lily roots!" sobbed the boy.

"I see", said the old lady. She felt sorry for him, so she went and gathered some of the ordinary lily roots. She worked hard, and gathered a whole sackful. Then she gathered firewood and lit a fire. She prepared the roots and cooked them. Then she said, "Come and eat these lily roots."

The orphan took one look, and cried even louder: "I don't want those lily roots. I don't like them. I want the special ones!"

And he went on crying.

Then one of the men got up, and went to a tree where he knew he could get wild honey. He brought some back, showed it to the boy, and said, "Look, wild honey! Come and eat some."

But the orphan only cried louder, and said, "I don't want honey, I want special lily roots!"

"All right, cry", said the man. "I'll have the honey."

Another woman went out with her digging stick, and dug up some yams. She gathered firewood, lit a fire, and roasted the yams. When they were ready she said to the boy, "Come and eat some yams."

But the orphan only cried and said, "I don't want yams, I want special lily roots!"

So the people all sat down and said to the orphan, "Well, you'll just have to cry. We offered you lily roots, and honey, and yams, and you don't want any of it, so we'll eat them ourselves."

But still the boy cried. The old people knew the danger he was bringing on them all, and they said to him: "Why must you keep on crying? You'll wake the Rainbow Snake, and she'll be angry. She taught us to gather food, and to eat whatever the land offers us. She'll eat us all alive if we don't do what she taught us!"

But the boy would not stop crying. At last, the noise he was making reached the ears of the Rainbow Snake who lay sleeping far to the north. She lifted her head, and said, "Who is making all that noise?"

She turned her head this way and that way, and she heard the crying noise coming from the south. The Rainbow Snake bent her head to the ground, and began to burrow through it. On and on she went, through sand, through soil, through solid rock, burrowing southward towards the noise of the orphan crying. When she came near, she lifted her head out of the earth, and saw the camp site where the orphan was still crying. The people looked up, and saw a flash of something bright to the north.

"It's her!" cried the old people. "It's the Rainbow Snake! Quick, run! No point trying to use your spears, no spear can hurt the Rainbow Snake. Run! Run!"

But before the people could leap to their feet and escape, the Rainbow Snake threw a loop of her tail round the whole camp, and dragged the people towards her. With one gulp, she swallowed the men, the women and the children, and the orphan boy, still crying. And they were never seen again.

Tales from the Buddhists

Prince Siddharta, the Buddha

Prince Siddharta was born in India two and a half thousand years ago. The king, his father, wanted Siddharta to become a great ruler. He wanted him to enjoy the life of a king. He did not want him to learn about the pain and suffering in the world. And so the king made sure that his young son grew up surrounded by wealth and luxury. Siddharta always had delicious food to eat. He always had beautiful clothes to wear. The palace was filled with people laughing and joking, singing and dancing. This was the only sort of life the prince knew. He did not know that outside the palace grounds there were people who were hungry, for they had nothing to eat. He did not know that there were people who were old and sick. He did not know that people died.

Siddharta was happy. When he grew up he married and had a baby son. He believed that he had everything he could ever want, and it seemed to him that life would go on this way for ever. But Siddharta was curious about life away from the palace, and one day he persuaded his charioteer to take him out into the countryside. Soon after they had left the palace, Siddharta saw something he had never seen before. He saw by the roadside an old man bent over his stick, walking slowly along the road.

"Stop, stop the horses!" Siddharta cried to his charioteer. "Why is that man walking so slowly? What is wrong with him? Why does he suffer so?"

"Master," replied his charioteer, "the man is old, and that is why he walks so slowly. We will all grow old one day." And he drove on.

But soon Siddharta called his charioteer to stop again. There, by the roadside, sat a crippled man. He could not walk and his body was covered in scars.

"What's wrong with him?" cried Siddharta. "Why does he look like that? Why is he in such pain?"

"He is ill", replied the charioteer. "He has a terrible disease which gives him the pain." And he drove on once more.

Next the prince saw a funeral procession. Some men were carrying a dead body through the streets. Other men and women followed. They were weeping and crying. Once more Siddharta stopped the charioteer and asked him the meaning of what he saw. The charioteer told him that everyone dies, and that friends and relatives weep when someone they love dies.

Last of all Siddharta saw a man who had no hair on his head, and was dressed in a yellow cloth.

"What is he doing?" Siddharta again asked his charioteer. "Why does he look like that?"

"He is a monk", the charioteer replied. "He has shaved his head to show that he has given up all wealth. He goes from place to place trying to find the truth. He owns nothing, he lives outside in the open, and he begs for small pieces of food."

Siddharta told his charioteer that it was time to take him home to the palace. He tried to enjoy palace life as he had done before, but he couldn't. He tried to enjoy the food and the clothes. He tried to enjoy the company of his friends and his family but he couldn't. All he could think about was what he had seen. He thought of the old man and the pain of growing old. What would it be like when he grew old? What would it be like for his family and friends to grow old? He thought too of the sick man and all his suffering. What if he, Siddharta, grew sick? What if his wife or baby son grew sick? Even thinking about it gave him pain. And he thought of the funeral procession. He loved this life; why should he die? He loved his wife and child; would they too die? He felt pain, and it seemed to him that everyone, everywhere, felt pain and suffering in their lives at some time, and he wanted to know why.

Last of all Siddharta remembered the monk, and he realized that he too wanted to be a monk. Life at the palace had no joy any more; he must go and somehow find out why people suffer.

So early one morning he crept into the room where his wife and son lay sleeping, and silently wished them goodbye. His charioteer drove him away from the palace to start a new life.

They stopped at the edge of a forest and there Siddharta prepared himself to be a monk. He changed his princely clothes for the simple robe of the charioteer. He shaved his head and he washed himself in the stream. Now he no longer looked like a prince, and he set forth to live the life of a monk.

For six long years he wandered through the forest with five other monks. He slept in the open and ate only a little food each day, sometimes just a grain of rice. He grew thinner and thinner, weaker and weaker. At last he knew he would not find an answer in this way. So he began to eat properly again, but his five companion monks left him. They were disgusted with him for they felt he had given in by eating.

So now Siddharta wandered through the forest all by himself. Often he felt lonely and he longed to see his wife and son once more. Then one evening he sat down under a fig tree. There he sat and sat, and thought and thought. He felt grief because he wanted to be with his family. How wonderful it would be to return to them and the comfort of the palace. But he knew he would never find an answer to pain and suffering if he did. So he continued to think and think and think, until he could no longer think. Until there was nothing left to think about, and his mind stopped working, and then he began to find peace. He forgot about himself and all his longings. He forgot his worries about growing old and about sickness and dying; and as he forgot his needs and his fears he found peace. Buddhists say he became an enlightened person, a Buddha. It was almost like going to sleep, and waking up to see the world differently.

Siddharta, the Buddha, wanted to stay under the fig tree for ever but he also wanted to share his new knowledge with others. He wanted others to find this peace that he had found. He left his tree and began to walk all over India, teaching anyone who would listen. The Buddha taught his followers that if they stopped worrying and stopped trying to be happy, then they would be truly happy. He taught them to stop worrying about getting ill, or growing old or dying. If they stopped worrying then they would find peace instead of pain.

And many, many people did listen to what Prince Siddharta, the Buddha said. They said to themselves that he was teaching them something which was important and true. And today there are many people all over the world who follow the teachings of Siddharta, the Buddha.

Note:
This story can be told in conjunction with the work on 'Attitudes to money' in the *Junior Teacher's Handbook*, pages 64 & 65.

The Hare-Mark on the Moon

Buddhists believe that the Buddha, who is all-knowing, has been reborn on Earth many times in many forms – as a man, as an animal and as a spirit. In the Jataka book there are stories about 550 of his lives. This is one of them.

L ong ago the future Buddha was born as a hare, and lived in a forest. He had three wise friends, Monkey, Jackal and Otter.

The animals all led good lives, and Hare reminded them not to eat on the holy fast-days and to give food to whoever asked them for it.

Then, one day, the animals were seeking food as usual. Otter caught a fish, Jackal caught some meat and Monkey found three mangoes. But Hare lay in his hole feeling too upset to go and eat his grass. He had just realised that if anyone asked him for food, he would have nothing to give to them.

"What can I do if someone asks me for a gift of food?" he thought. "All I have is grass, and that's no good to anyone but a hare."

Then a solution came to him. If someone asked him for food, he would give up his own body to feed them. So unselfish was this thought that it reached Sakra on his throne in Heaven.

Sakra decided to see for himself if Hare was truly this noble. He went down to earth and took the shape of a holy man, called a Brahman. First, he went to Otter and asked him for food. Otter offered him his fish. Then he went to Jackal and Monkey and they offered him meat and mangoes. Sakra said thank you but did not take their food.

Next, he went to Hare. Hare was overjoyed to have the chance to give.

"Brahman," he said, "today I will give as I have never given before." He told the holy man to gather wood and light a fire. When the fire was crackling brightly, Hare threw himself into it. But the flames around him were as cool as the air in his burrow. He stood on the blazing logs and looked at Sakra in surprise.

"Brahman, what has happened to your fire?" he asked.

"I am Sakra", said Sakra. "I have come down from Heaven to test your generosity, and you have shown me that it is as endless as the universe."

Sakra then tucked the hare under one arm and picked up a mountain with the other.

"Wise hare, your virtue will be seen by all creation until the end of this world cycle", he said.

Sakra squeezed the mountain and used its juice as ink to draw an outline of the hare on the moon. Then he put Hare back down in a field of grass and returned to Heaven. And that is why today there is picture of a hare on the moon.

Note:
This story can be told in conjunction with work on 'The natural world' in the *Junior Assembly Book*, page 15.

The Monkey Bridge

I t is said that the Buddha had many other lives before he became the Buddha, the enlightened one. In one of these previous lives he was born as the king of the monkeys who lived in the Himalayan forests.

In the heart of these forests, by a river where no one ever ventured, stood a thousand-year-old tree. Every year the boughs of this ancient tree were laden with enormous golden fruit. No other tree bore such delicious fruit. But all the forest creatures dreaded one of these fruits falling into the river and being swept down the mountains to the kingdom of humans. For it was said that a terrible greed burned in the hearts of humans, and that once they had tasted the golden fruit their greed would rage like fire and devour everything in its path: the tree of golden fruit, the forest itself, everything would be in peril.

To prevent this happening, the monkeys checked the branches of the great tree every day to make sure no fruit was so ripe that it would drop of its own accord. But one fruit grew beneath a large leaf, where it ripened unseen until one day it dropped – into the river! The monkeys watched helplessly as the golden fruit was whirled away on the river water.

It journeyed on, spinning in the strong current as the river crossed the plains. Eventually, it was captured by a washerwoman who traded it for a piece of bright cloth. The cloth trader sold it to a landowner for the price of a small elephant. The landowner gave it to a soldier as a fee for his services. The soldier presented it to the king, who ate it. The king had never tasted such delicious fruit before, and immediately asked where it had come from. Before long the washerwoman was found, and when she explained where she had found the fruit, the king decided to set off up the river to find the tree which bore such wonderful fruit.

The following morning the king's army was cutting a great swathe up the mountain in search of the tree whose fruit tasted of heaven. The forest throbbed with fear. The monkeys lined the branches of the ancient tree armed with only nuts and cones as the human army surrounded it, their swords gleaming, cruel as winter ice.

But the battle was lost before it had begun. The monkey king ordered a retreat to the far side of the river, but none of the monkeys dared to jump over the river. The river was too wide and wild and they were too small. Only their king had the size and power to leap the distance.

And so he did, landing in a clump of elephant grass. From it he pulled out the longest strand, ten times the length of his own tail, and just long enough to form a bridge across the river. He tied one end to a stout tree and the other to his foot, forgetting that in tying it he had also shortened it! So when he leapt back to his stranded followers his arms could only just reach the nearest branch of the ancient tree. The rest of his body became part of the bridge.

"Over my back! Over my back!" he called to the monkeys. They hesitated, caught between their fear of the soldiers, now climbing the tree, and their fear for their leader whose powerful body seemed suddenly small and frail as it hung over the river.

"Over my back!" he called again. "I command you!"

The monkeys obeyed, one by one. Their king's breath came in short gasps of pain as they did so, on and on until, as the last one crossed, his strength gave out, and his back broke.

As the monkey king clung dying to the branch, the human king reached down in pity and freed him. Wrapping him in his own cloak he lifted him on to the ancient tree.

"You are the mightiest of the monkeys", he said. "Why did you sacrifice your own life for those who are weaker than you?"

"It is the duty of a king to love and protect his subjects", said the future Buddha. "It is that, not might, that makes a king. I give my life with joy."

Then he closed his eyes and died.

Before they returned to the plain the humans built a temple to honour the monkey king, and the human king swore to protect the forest and all its creatures with the same love that the monkey king had shown.

Note:
This story can be told in conjunction with work on 'Good Friday' and 'The natural world' in the *Junior Assembly Book*, pages 7 & 15.

Tales from Christianity

The Christmas Story

A version for infants

1. Mary and the Angel

In a little village called Nazareth, in the land of Israel, many years ago there lived a young woman called Mary. She was a fairly ordinary girl. She lived with her mother and father and she helped them in the house. She was nearly grown up, and she was soon going to be married to a man called Joseph.

Then one day an angel sent from God appeared to Mary as she sat alone in the house.

"Greetings, Mary," he said, "I have a message for you from God. He has chosen you for something very special. You will have a baby boy. The baby will be God's son. He will be a blessing to all the people in the world."

Mary was puzzled and frightened when she heard this. What could it mean?

"Do not be frightened", said the angel. "God will look after you. Trust in his power."

Mary answered, "I am God's servant. Whatever he wants, I will do it." And the angel went away.

Mary thought for a long time about what he had said. She was happy that God was going to send his son to help people, and she felt very proud that God had chosen her to be his mother.

2. *The Journey to Bethlehem*

A few months passed, and Mary married Joseph. Joseph knew that Mary's baby was going to be a special child of God, and he too felt very proud that he was going to help look after God's son.

As the baby grew inside Mary, he took great care of her, and made sure that she did not get too tired.

But then they heard about a new law: "Every man must go back to the place where he was born, and stay there while all the people are counted. You must take your families with you."

"Oh dear!" said Joseph. "That means we must go to Bethlehem. I was born in Bethlehem. How are we to get there? It is many many miles, and you cannot walk so far now that the baby is so big inside you."

In those days there were no cars, or buses, or trains. Rich people had horses to ride, and only very, very rich people had carriages. Joseph thought and thought. How could Mary travel to Bethlehem? She would have to ride his donkey, but he was still worried.

"The donkey is small and difficult to ride", he said to Mary. "I am sure you will get too tired."

But Mary remembered what the angel said, "Trust in God's power". She smiled at Joseph. "Don't worry", she said. "God will look after me. Look, he has given me a donkey to ride. He will give me anything else I need."

So Mary and Joseph loaded up the donkey with all the things they knew they would need on the journey. They could not take too much, because the donkey was very small. They took some food and a little bit of money. They took blankets, for the nights were cold. And Mary took a few pieces of cloth to wrap her baby in when he was born, because she knew that they might still be many miles from home when the time came for his birth.

And so they set off. It was a very hard journey, and Mary did get very tired. It took them several days, and they had to sleep on the ground at night. But everywhere they went, there were people travelling, all going back to the place where they were born, as the law said. And everywhere they went, people were kind to Mary. They shared their food with her. They lent her an extra blanket to sleep on, and they found her the best place to sleep. And so, as they went, Mary knew that God was looking after her, just as the angel had promised.

At last, at the end of a long day, they arrived in Bethlehem.

"Well, at last we have arrived", said Joseph. "Now you will be able to sleep in an inn tonight and be comfortable."

"I am glad," said Mary, "for I think the baby will be born very soon."

And so, weary but glad their journey was finally over, they came to Bethlehem.

3. Jesus is Born

Mary and Joseph had arrived in Bethlehem, but their troubles were not over. Many, many people had been born in Bethlehem. They had all come back, with their families, to be counted. And they all wanted to stay at an inn.

At the first inn, Mary and Joseph knocked on the door.

"Please, sir, have you got a room for me and my wife?" asked Joseph.

"No," said the innkeeper, "we don't want any poor people staying here."

So on they went to the next inn.

"Please, sir, have you got a room for me and my wife?" asked Joseph.

"No," said the innkeeper, "you are too dirty from the journey."

So on they went to the next inn.

"Please, sir, have you got a room for me and my wife?" asked Joseph.

"No, I'm sorry," said the innkeeper, "we have no room." But he looked kindly at Mary and Joseph. He saw that Mary was very tired. He saw that she was going to have a baby. Mary smiled at him. She knew God would look after her.

"Please," said Joseph, "we have nowhere else to go."

"Well," said the innkeeper, "there's no room in the inn, but there is a stable at the back. It's warm and dry, and there's some straw you can sleep on. It's better than nothing, but ..."

"Oh, thank you, thank you", said Mary. "Let us stay there."

So the innkeeper led them into the tiny, dark stable, gave them a lantern, and left them there. And that night, with no one there to help her but Joseph, and no one there to see but the animals, Mary's baby was born. She called him 'Jesus'. She wrapped him in the pieces of cloth she had brought, and laid him in the manger full of hay.

"At last, he is here", she whispered. "I knew God would look after me."

4. *The Shepherds*

On the same night that the baby Jesus was born in the stable, there were some shepherds out on the hillside near Bethlehem. Every night they stayed out in the fields to look after their sheep. It was late in the night, and it was dark in the fields, apart from the glow of the fire and the light of the stars. The shepherds were sleepy, but just awake enough to watch for wolves and other dangers. Even the sheep were quiet. Suddenly, the sky became light, brighter than the brightest summer day.

"What is it?" cried the shepherds. They were dazzled by the light, and they couldn't see. They were very frightened.

Then a voice came from the sky.

"Do not be afraid", said the voice. "I am bringing you good news!"

Slowly, the shepherds looked up. Their eyes got used to the bright light. And there in the sky they saw an angel, as bright as the sun.

"Yes," said the angel, "this is news that will make everyone in the world happy. But you are the first to hear it. A baby has been born in Bethlehem. He is God's son. He has come to help everyone in the world. Go to Bethlehem and see him. You will find him wrapped in pieces of cloth, and lying in a manger."

Then the shepherds heard the most beautiful sound they had ever heard. Thousands of voices were singing. They could see the sky was full of angels. The shepherds wished they could listen to that music for ever.

"Glory to God", sang the angels. "Peace on earth. God is showing his love for all the world."

And then it was over. The angel voices were quiet. The darkness returned to the hillside.

"Was it a dream?" said the shepherds to each other. Then one of them said, "Let us go to Bethlehem, and see."

So they left their sheep in the field, and set off. And when they came to Bethlehem, they found everything just as the angel had said. They found the stable, and Joseph and Mary, and they found the baby lying in the manger. Very, very quietly, they gathered round the manger and looked at the baby. They knew he was God's special baby.

"He is here", they whispered. "God is showing his love for all the world."

5. *The Wise Men*

In another country, far, far away from Bethlehem, three men were also awake that night. They were wise men who had read many books and thought many thoughts. They were awake because they liked to watch the stars together. They knew all about the stars and planets – where each one was, and how bright it should be. They stood on the top of the hill, and quietly watched the sky. Then one of them pointed.

"Look," he said, "there, in the east. I have never seen that star before."

"No," said the others, "It is a new star. And look how bright it is! It must mean something special."

"I think I know what it means", said the first wise man. "A new king has been born, a king of heaven and earth. We must go to greet him and take him gifts."

"How will we find him?" asked the others.

"We will follow the star, and it will lead us to him", said the first wise man.

So they got their gifts ready, and set off to find the new king of heaven and earth.

They took gold, because he was king of the earth.

They took frankincense, because he was king of heaven.

And they took myrrh, because they knew that one day the king would die.

On and on they travelled, through towns and villages, through woods and deserts, by day and by night. At last they came to the great city of Jerusalem.

"Where is the new king?" they asked.

The people in Jerusalem didn't know about Jesus, the king of heaven and earth. They only knew about King Herod, who lived in the palace. So they took the wise men to the palace.

"Where is the king?" they asked King Herod. "The new king, who has just been born?"

King Herod was angry. "I am the king", he said to himself. "I don't want a new king."

But he smiled at the wise men, and he called his own wise men who lived in his palace.

"What does it say in your books?" he asked. "Where will the king of heaven and earth be born?"

"They say it will be in Bethlehem", answered the king's wise men.

"Go and look in Bethlehem," the king told the wise men, "and when you find the new king, come and tell me. I would like to see him too."

But secretly, he thought, "When I find him I will kill him."

The wise men left king Herod's palace, and went to Bethlehem. And still the star which they had seen went ahead of them, until at last it led them to where the baby Jesus lay. It was a poor, dark and dirty place, but the wise men went in. They knelt down by the baby and offered him their gifts: gold, frankincense and myrrh.

They looked at each other in the dim light, and smiled.

"He is here", they whispered. "The king of heaven and earth is born."

6. To Egypt

After the wise men had seen Jesus, it was time for them to go home. But one of them had a dream. He told the others.

"We must not go back to King Herod", he said. "We must go straight home. I do not know why, but we must not go back to Jerusalem." So they set off for home.

Very soon Joseph too had a dream. In his dream he saw an angel who said to him: "The baby Jesus is in danger. You must not stay here. Take Mary and the baby, and go as quickly as you can to Egypt. There you will be safe."

Jesus and Mary and Joseph lived safely in Egypt until they heard that King Herod had died. Then, at long last, they packed their bags, and loaded up their donkey, and set off on the long journey home – back to Nazareth, where the story started.

Note:
Further information on Christmas and the Nativity story can be found in the *Infant Teacher's Handbook*, pages 68-73 & 79, and in the *Junior Teacher's Handbook*, pages 8, 88 & 111.

The Call to the Disciples

When Jesus grew up, he began to travel round the countryside and villages, teaching people and telling them about God. There was a big lake near where Jesus lived, called the Lake of Galilee, and Jesus often walked by the lake and talked with people who came to see him there. It was quite a busy place, with fishing boats sailing out on to the lake, people buying and selling fish on the shore, and fishermen working in their boats and mending the nets they used to catch the fish.

One day, when he was teaching the people about God on the shore of the lake, there were so many people crowded round him that those at the back could not see him, or hear what he was saying.

Jesus looked around him and, there, on the beach, was a big boat which belonged to one of the fishermen.

"Is this your boat?" he said to the man standing by it.

"Yes, sir", said the fisherman. "My name is Simon, and this boat belongs to me and my brother Andrew."

"Simon," said Jesus, "will you do me a favour?"

"Of course," said Simon, "what is it?"

"Let me get in your boat," said Jesus, "and then sail me out just a little way on to the lake. That way I can talk to all these people without them crowding round too close. Everyone will be able to see me and hear what I am saying."

So Jesus sat down in the front of the boat, and Simon sailed it out on to the water, and stopped where everyone could see Jesus. And Jesus spoke to the people. He told them stories – stories that made them think about what God is like. He told them about how much God loved them and wanted them to love him. And he told them how all the wrong things they had done would be all right if they only said that they were sorry to God and tried to do better. Simon sat in his boat and listened to Jesus. And, as he listened, he thought: "What a wonderful man Jesus is! How I would love to be with him all the time. Then I could hear more of the stories, and he would explain all the parts that I don't understand. And he would teach me how to be a better person, and maybe I wouldn't be so impatient with people, and wouldn't get in a bad temper so often."

When Jesus had finished speaking to the people, he turned to Simon and he said: "Thank you for lending me your boat, Simon. Now you had better get on with your job of catching fish. Sail out a bit further, and put your nets over the side of the boat."

"Well," said Simon, "we fished all last night and didn't catch anything. I don't think there are any fish in this part of the lake at the moment. But if you tell me to, I will see what we can catch."

So Simon and his brother Andrew put the nets over the side of the boat. Almost at once, the nets began to feel heavy. "We have caught thousands of fish!" shouted Simon. "Quick, Andrew! Help me pull them in!"

"I can't!" gasped Andrew, as he pulled at the net. "It's too heavy for one boat. Look, over there! There's James and his brother John in their boat. Give them a shout, and get them to come over and help us!"

So they called to their friends in the other boat, and between them they pulled and they heaved, and at last they got their great catch of fish in to land. When they had finished, Simon and Andrew and James and John stood there out of breath. They looked at Jesus, and Simon shook his head. He was puzzled, and a bit nervous.

"You make me afraid, sir", he said. "You make things happen that I don't understand. Perhaps you'd better go away."

"It's all right, Simon," said Jesus, "there's nothing to be afraid of. I want you to follow me and be with me always. From now on it is not thousands of fish you will catch, but thousands of people. You will catch them and bring them to God."

And from that day onwards, Simon and Andrew and James and John went everywhere with Jesus. There were other friends who went everywhere with Jesus, too. Jesus had asked them to be with him, just as he had asked Simon and Andrew and James and John to be with him. Altogether there were twelve of Jesus' special friends. They learnt all that he taught them, and they saw how he cured people who were sick, and made sad people happy again. And after he left them and went up to heaven, those special friends of Jesus carried on his work. They taught people about God, they made sick people better, and they taught people how to love Jesus, just as they did.

Zacchaeus

Many years ago, in the town of Jericho, lived a man named Zacchaeus. He was a rich man, but he was not very happy, because people didn't like him. This was hardly surprising: the reason he was rich was that he was a tax collector, and in those days tax-collectors made most of their money by cheating people.

Then, one day, Zacchaeus heard that someone special was coming to Jericho: the new teacher, Jesus, whom everyone was talking about. As he listened to the stories people were telling about Jesus, Zacchaeus thought: "I wish I could see him. He sounds like someone important. But I'm so short I'll never manage it – there are sure to be crowds of people, and I won't be able to see a thing."

Then Zacchaeus had an idea. He would climb a tree! There, just by the road, that one would be perfect! So he began to climb up into the branches. It wasn't easy: all that rich food had left him plump and not very fit, but he scrambled up, puffing and grunting, until at last he was on a high, sturdy branch. He could see everything from up here.

Down below, everyone was pushing and shoving. "Is he here yet?" "What does he look like?" "I think ... yes, I can see him ... there he is!" And up above them all, Zacchaeus watched as Jesus drew nearer and nearer. Soon he would be passing the tree. Yes, here he was, just about to go past – but no, Jesus had stopped. He was right underneath the tree! And he was looking straight up through the branches, straight up at Zacchaeus.

Zacchaeus didn't know what to do. Jesus was looking at him. Not only that, he was speaking to him – to him, Zacchaeus the tax collector! "Hurry up and come down, Zacchaeus," said Jesus, "I'm staying at your house today."

Zacchaeus couldn't climb down fast enough – he was so pleased. Jesus had noticed him, and wanted to spend time with him! Other people weren't so happy. They started muttering, "Doesn't Jesus know who this man is? He's a tax-collector, a swindler, not a respectable person at all!" But Jesus didn't take any notice. He knew what he was doing.

When Zacchaeus stood in front of Jesus, he realised that he needed to change his life. He said, "Lord, I want to give half of everything I own to the poor. If I've swindled anyone out of money, I will pay it back four times over."

Jesus said, "Today salvation has come to your house. I have come to rescue those who, like you, are lost."

Note:
This story can be told in conjunction with work on the unit 'Unlikely friends', *Junior Teacher's Handbook*, page 31.

Loaves and Fishes

W hen Jesus was about thirty years old, he began to travel round his home area of Galilee, healing the sick and teaching people about God. He did many marvellous things to help people, and there was something about his teaching that made people want to hear more and more. Every day they came to Jesus, no matter where he was. Every time he moved to another village, word spread round the countryside, and crowds rushed to see him. They thronged round him, telling him their troubles, asking his advice, and pushing their children forward for him to touch them and bless them.

Jesus loved the people, and he knew that God had sent him just for this, to show God's love for all people. So day after day, from dawn to dusk, he welcomed the people who came to him. But Jesus knew this could not go on. One evening he gathered his special friends, his disciples, round him, and said: "I need time to pray and be with God alone. All my power and all my love come from him. I cannot stop praying. And you, my disciples, you need time to be quiet with me, to ask me questions and learn what I have to teach you."

So very early the next morning, long before it was light, Jesus and his disciples set off secretly from the place where they were staying, and went up into the hills. They left the fertile areas where there were many farms, and they left the gentle slopes where shepherds grazed their flocks, and they walked onward and upward to the loneliest place they could find, away from houses and roads and the business of life. And there they sat down and spent time in quiet prayer to God.

No one knew how word got out. Perhaps some wakeful shepherd had seen them set out through the fields. Perhaps a sharp-eyed child had caught a glimpse of their coloured cloaks from across the valley. However it happened – by midday there was a steady stream of people making their way up the steep hill path to see Jesus. By the afternoon there were thousands of them. Jesus looked at the people and sighed.

"They are like sheep without a shepherd", he said. "How can I refuse to help them, even for one day?" And he sat down on a rock and began to teach the people.

For the people listening to Jesus time seemed to fly by. They thought of nothing but the words he was saying. It was the disciples who first noticed the problem. The sun was getting low in the sky. They were miles from anywhere, and no one in the crowd had eaten anything all day.

"Master," they said to Jesus, "send the people away now. Perhaps it is not too late for them to find food to buy at some of the scattered farmhouses, if they all split up now."

"There's no need for them to go", said Jesus. "We shall give them something to eat."

The disciples looked at each other. What on earth did he mean?

"Master," they said, "even two hundred silver coins would only buy enough food for each person to have a tiny piece each. How can we possibly feed them all?"

But just then one of the disciples came up and said, "There is a boy here who has five loaves and two small fish. But it is a small amount of food – nothing between so many people."

"Bring him here," said Jesus, "and ask the people to sit down in groups."

So the boy came and gave all the food he had to Jesus. Jesus took the loaves and the two small fish, and gave thanks to God for them. Then he broke them and handed the pieces to his disciples to hand out to the people. Backwards and forwards they went among the people, handing out more whenever people had finished, until everyone had eaten all they wanted. Then Jesus said, "There must be no waste. Go round and gather up all the scraps." So the disciples did, and when they gathered together all the leftover food from those five thousand people, they found that they had twelve baskets full.

Note:
This story can be told in conjunction with work on 'Sharing food' in the *Junior Teacher's Handbook*, page 34.

Jairus' Daughter

When Jesus was about thirty years old, he spent a lot of time teaching people and helping them. If people were sick, or could not walk, he made them better. If they were blind, he made them see again. If they were sad, he made them happy again. Hundreds of people came to see Jesus every day. Some came because they wanted him to help them; some came just to hear him speak and to listen to the stories he told.

Then, one day, a man came pushing his way through the crowd that surrounded Jesus, shouting and crying. "Jesus! Jesus! Help me, please! You are the only one who can help me now!"

When the people heard him, they made room for him and led him up to Jesus.

"This is Jairus", they said. "He is an important man in our synagogue. What's the matter, Jairus?"

Jairus was so upset that he fell down at Jesus' feet. "It's my daughter!" he sobbed. "She's only young, and she's very, very ill. I think ... I think she's going to die!"

Jesus bent down and lifted him up. "Don't cry, Jairus. I'll come at once." And they set off through the crowd of people. But it was slow going. Jairus was pushing people, and calling out: "Let us through, let us through. Please! My daughter is ill! Let Jesus come to her!"

But just then Jairus' servant arrived from Jairus' house. "I'm... I'm sorry, master," he said, "but your daughter has died. There is no need to bother Jesus any more. It is too late."

When he heard this, Jairus turned to Jesus and began to say, "Goodbye, and thank you for trying to help."

But Jesus said, "Don't worry, Jairus, your daughter is safe. Only believe in me, and everything will be all right." He went on pushing his way towards Jairus' house.

When they got there, they found all Jairus' family and friends outside the house, crying for the little girl who had died.

"Shsh..." said Jesus. "There is no need to cry. The little girl is only asleep." But the people in the house knew that she was dead, and they thought that Jesus was being very foolish and silly to say she wasn't.

Jesus told everyone to stay outside the house and be quiet, and he went in with Peter and James and John, three of his special friends, and Jairus and his wife. "When she wakes up", he said, "she will be frightened if there are a lot of people round her making a noise."

Jesus went into the little girl's bedroom, and saw her body lying on the bed. He went up to her, and took her by the hand, and said, very gently, "Little girl! Little girl! Wake up now". At once the little girl got up.

"There," said Jesus, "she's all right now. I expect she's hungry, though, after that long illness. Give her something to eat."

And as Jesus left the house, he looked back at the girl's mother and father as they sat laughing and hugging their little girl, and feeding her with all the best things they could find – dates and honey, and milk and grapes.

⸻

Mary and Martha

Jesus had a lot of friends. Some of his friends were people that he had cured of their illnesses. Some of his friends were people others didn't like, but Jesus taught them how to be better people. Some of his friends were men who travelled round with him wherever he went, and heard him teach large crowds of people. Some of his friends lived far away, and Jesus came to visit them whenever he could. Whenever Jesus was in their village they would invite him to their house to stay, and they would give him the best food they had, and the best room with the best bed, because they loved him so much.

Two of these friends were two sisters called Mary and Martha. They lived with their brother Lazarus in a village called Bethany.

One day, Martha came home from the market, very excited. "Mary, Mary!" she called. "I've just heard. Jesus is coming. He's in the next village and he'll be here for supper tonight. I must start cooking, quick. Now, where is my mixing bowl? No, first I must go out and buy some of the best fruit for Jesus, then I'll start to cook, then I'll tidy up. No, then I'll wash the best dishes, or maybe I should run round and ask the neighbours if they would like to come to supper too. Oh dear, there's so much to do, I don't know whether I'm coming or going today!"

"Is he really coming?" said Mary, smiling. "I'm so glad. I love to hear him talking – he makes me understand things I didn't understand before. And he tells such wonderful stories!"

"Talking? Stories?" exclaimed Martha. "We've got no time for talking and stories today, sister! We've got to get everything ready. Everything must be perfect for our friend Jesus. You love him just as much as I do, don't you? So help me cook the best meal he's ever had, and get a comfortable bed ready for him. Come on, quick!"

And Martha bustled away, muttering to herself, and marking off on her fingers all the things she had to do. Mary smiled at her, and picked up a broom and duster and went to prepare the room where Jesus was going to sleep. The sisters worked all day. Martha ran from one job to the next without stopping. But every now and then, between jobs, Mary would stop, and smile, and say to herself, "He is coming! How happy I will be to see him!"

At last Jesus came to the door. Mary and Martha were both very happy to see him. Martha ran to fetch water to wash his feet, as was the custom of the time, while Mary sat down beside him so that she could hear what he had to say. She sat and sat, and listened and listened, and the more she heard, the more she loved him. She felt as if she could sit there all day listening to what he had to say.

Meanwhile Martha was running about, getting the meal ready, making sure the best plates were on the table, and welcoming the neighbours. She looked at Mary once or twice, and frowned at her, but Mary did not even see her. Mary did not help with the cooking or with putting the meal on the table. She just sat with Jesus.

At last Martha got very angry. She went up to Jesus and said: "Don't you care that I am doing all the work and Mary is just sitting here? It's not fair! Tell her to come and help me!"

Jesus looked at her, and he smiled. He reached out and took her hand, and made her sit down near him.

"Martha," he said, "you are worried and fretting about too many things. There's no need for all this fuss. I don't need a special meal when I come to see you. I don't need the best plates. I don't need a big party. I came to see you and Mary, my friends, and to tell you about God, my father in heaven. That is the only important thing. Mary knew that, and she came to listen to me. Leave all your housework now, and come and sit down with us."

Some Parables of Jesus

Jesus often told stories to explain to people what God is like. Especially, he wanted to tell people how much God loves them. Here are some of the stories he told.

1. The Lost Sheep

Once upon a time there was a shepherd. He had a hundred sheep, and he loved them all. Every day he led them out to where the grass was greenest, and he watched over them while they grazed. Every evening he led them back to the sheepfold. There he counted them as they went in.

"One, two, three, four, five,..." and so on until he counted, "ninety-seven, ninety-eight, ninety-nine, a hundred."

When he was sure that all one hundred sheep were safe, he settled down for the night with his friends in the shepherds' hut.

One evening he led the sheep back to the sheepfold as usual, and as usual he counted them as they went in.

"One, two, three, four, five,..." and then, "ninety-seven, ninety-eight, ninety-nine..."

He stopped. There were only ninety-nine sheep! Surely he must have counted wrong! He drove all the sheep out of the sheepfold, and counted them in again. But still it came to ninety-nine. One of them must be lost, out there in the dark fields. He knew which one it was – one of the youngest sheep in the flock. It would be frightened out there, and there were wild animals that might kill it.

"Never mind," said his friends, "you still have ninety-nine sheep. That lost one is only small, and not very important. It'll probably turn up in the morning."

"No," said the shepherd, "all my sheep are important to me. I cannot rest until I find this lost little one."

So he took a lantern and set off in the dark. He looked in fields and woods; he looked up hills and down valleys; he looked down little paths and behind great rocks. And at last he found his lost little sheep, cowering behind a thorn bush, hiding from the wild animals. He picked it up, and he could feel the little body trembling with cold and fear. With a happy heart, he carried the sheep home, and put it safely in the sheepfold.

Then, when he was sure his sheep were all safe, he settled down with his friends to sleep.

Jesus said: "God loves you even more than that shepherd loved his sheep. When any of you are lost or frightened, God comes to find you, even if you are small and think you are not important. He will not rest until you are safe."

12/02

2. *The Prodigal Son*

Once upon a time there was a father who had two sons. He owned a farm, and his two sons worked on the farm with him. They knew that when their father died, they would share his farm and his money between them.

One day the younger son came to his father and said, "Father, I want to go off and enjoy myself now, not wait for when the farm and the money are mine. Couldn't you give me my share now?"

So his father gave him the money that would be his share, and the son went off to a city far away in another country. There he had a great time. He bought fine clothes, and good food. He invited important people to his house, and they came because he had plenty of money and gave good parties. He didn't do any work, but just went around enjoying himself all day.

But then things began to change. First of all, he soon found that he had spent all of his money. He went to the people he thought were his friends, but without his fine clothes and good food, they didn't want to be friends with him any more. The second thing that happened was even worse.

There was a famine in the land, and there was not enough for anyone to eat. Food was more and more expensive, and the young man could not buy anything to eat at all. He tried to find a job to earn some money so he could eat, but the only job he could find was looking after pigs, which to Jews are unclean animals. It was a horrible job, but he had to do it or he would have starved to death. As it was he could hardly get enough food to keep him alive. He was so hungry that he felt like eating the pigs' food. He sat, cold and hungry in the woods with the pigs.

"What a fool I am!" he said to himself. "I should never have left home! But how can I go back now? I have spent all the money my father gave me, and now I have nothing. I am not fit to be called his son. But even my father's servants have a better life than I do now. I will go to him, and ask to be taken back as one of the servants, not as his son, for I do not deserve it."

So he set off towards home. He travelled many weary days, almost fainting with hunger. At last he came near to his home, and he felt more and more nervous about seeing his father.

But just as he came round the last bend in the road, his father happened to be looking out across the fields. He saw a feeble person, dressed in rags, come slowly round the bend in the road. And in spite of everything, in spite of the thinness, the rags, and the dirt, he recognised his son. At once he ran forward, calling to the servants: "Quick! Bring clothes, bring food and drink! Prepare a bath, and the best bed! My son has come home!"

The son began to say, "Please, father, forgive me. I cannot be called your son any more, but perhaps ..."

"My son, my son!" interrupted the father. "Of course you are still my son, and I am so happy to see you. I thought you were dead!"

So he welcomed his son back, and had a great feast. He invited all his friends.

"Rejoice with me, " he said, "for my son, who I thought was dead, is alive again. My son, who was lost, is found again!"

Jesus said: "God is like that father. Even when we go away from him; even when we waste the good things he gives us, even when we have done very bad things, he wants us to come back to him. He loves us, and will welcome us any time we ask."

3. *The Good Samaritan*

When Jesus was going around teaching, people often asked him difficult questions, hoping to catch him out. One day a lawyer came and said to him, "What must I do to live forever with God?"

Jesus answered with another question, "What does it say in the Laws of Moses, which have been handed down to you?"

The lawyer replied, "The Law says that I must love God with all my heart and all my soul, with all my strength and all my mind, and that I must love my neighbour as much as myself."

"That's right. Go and do as the Law says, and you will live with God."

"But who is my neighbour?" asked the lawyer.

Jesus answered by telling a story.

Once upon a time, a man was travelling from Jerusalem to Jericho. While he was travelling along, a band of robbers attacked him. They took his money, the donkey he was riding, even his clothes. Not only that, but they beat him up, knocked him out, and left him lying by the side of the road, half dead.

As he lay there, a priest came along the road. The priest saw the traveller lying there, covered in blood and bruises, and crossed to the other side of the road. He hurried on past as fast as he could, afraid that the robbers would attack him as well.

Then a Levite, a holy man, came by. He saw the poor wretch lying there, helpless and in pain, but he too passed by on the other side of the road.

The traveller was getting worse and worse as he lay there in the hot sun. At last, a Samaritan came to where he was lying. Now, Jews and Samaritans do not get along. Despite this, when the Samaritan saw the traveller, he felt sorry for him. He stopped his donkey, got down and bandaged the traveller's wounds. Then he picked him up, put him on the donkey and carried him to the nearest inn. He looked after him there all night.

The next day, the Samaritan had to leave on business. Before he left, he gave the innkeeper money to take care of the traveller until he was well again. He even said that, if it cost more, he would pay the difference on his return journey.

Jesus finished his story and asked the lawyer, "Who do you think was a neighbour to the man who was robbed?"

The lawyer replied, "The one who was kind to him."

"Then go and do as he did. That is what the law means by loving your neighbour."

4. The Unforgiving Servant

When Jesus wanted to teach people something important, he often told them a story which made it easier to remember. One day one of Jesus' friends asked him, "How many times should I forgive someone who treats me badly? As often as seven times?"

"Not seven times," Jesus answered, "but seventy-seven." And he told this story.

Once there was a king who decided to collect all the money people owed him. He checked his books and found that one of his servants owed him ten thousand silver coins. He called the servant to come before him but the servant did not have the money to pay him back. The king ordered that all the servant's possessions should be sold to pay off the debt.

"Not only that," he ordered, "but you and your family will be sold as slaves!"

The servant was very frightened; he fell to his knees and begged the king, "Wait for a while; be patient with me and I'll pay you back everything I owe you."

The king felt sorry for the servant and let him off the debt completely. On the way out, the servant met another servant who owed him a small sum of money. He grabbed this servant by the throat and said, "Pay back what you owe at once".

The other servant said to him, "Wait a while and I'll pay you everything I owe", but the first servant wouldn't listen. Instead he had him thrown into prison.

When the other servants saw what happened, they were very upset about it; they went and told the king all that had happened. The king called the servant back and said: "You wicked servant! I forgave you all your debts, because you pleaded with me. You should have forgiven your fellow servant just as I forgave you." The king was so angry that he sent the servant to jail, where he stayed until he could pay off his debt.

Note:
These stories can be told in conjunction with work in the *Infant Assembly Book*, page 49 and the *Junior Teacher's Handbook*, pages 17, 42 & 60 (The Good Samaritan) & 62 (The Prodigal Son and The Unforgiving Servant)).

The Easter Story

An Infant version

During his life Jesus made a lot of people angry. Some of the teachers didn't like him because the people listened to him and not to them. Some of the people in charge didn't like him because he taught people about the kingdom of God, and they thought Jesus would make their own kingdoms less important. And some people didn't like him because he told them that they were not as good as they thought they were.

So they got together and decided to kill Jesus.

"We could say he is a criminal and arrest him and kill him", said one.

"But he is always with his friends – his disciples – " said another. "And there are always crowds of people around him. They would never let us take him away."

But one of Jesus' disciples, called Judas, went to the people who hated Jesus and said: "If you give me money, I will show you where to find him when there are no crowds of people around. You will be able to arrest him then."

So they paid Judas the money, and waited for their chance.

Soon, there was a big festival, called 'Passover'. During Passover everyone stayed at home and had a special supper with their family and friends. Jesus and his friends stayed at home and ate their Passover supper, just like everyone else. But Jesus was sad as he sat with his friends.

"Very soon," he said, "people will come and take me away and kill me. But do not worry. After three days I will come back to life again."

A little while later, as Jesus sat with his friends in the garden, Judas went and fetched the soldiers. They arrested Jesus and took him away to kill him. In the morning they took him out of the town, and up a hill. There they nailed his hands and feet to a big wooden cross, and stood it upright and left him there until he died. That was what people did to criminals in those days. Jesus' friends watched, but they could do nothing to save him.

When the soldiers had made sure that Jesus was dead, they went away and left him. Slowly his friends gathered round, and very sadly they took his body down from the cross, wrapped it in clean sheets, and carried it to a cave, where they laid it down. Then, still crying, they rolled a large rock across the mouth of the cave so that no one could get in, and went home.

Three days later, very early in the morning, three women came to the cave. They were friends of Jesus, and they had come to see where his body lay. But when they got to the cave, they were very surprised. The great rock across the mouth of the cave had been rolled away. Jesus' body was not inside. Instead they saw an angel who said to them: "He is not here. He has come alive again. Go and tell all his friends."

At first the women did not understand how Jesus could be alive, when they knew he had died. But they went and told Simon Peter, and John, and all Jesus' other disciples. But the disciples did not believe what the women told them.

"You are so upset, you are just dreaming that Jesus is alive", they said. But the women insisted that what they had said was true, so Simon Peter and John went to the cave to see for themselves what had happened. They ran to the cave and saw everything just as the women had told them. They did not know what to think, and they went away.

But one of the women, called Mary, stayed behind. She thought that someone had taken Jesus' body away, and she sat there crying, because she wanted to see him again. Just then she heard a voice behind her.

"Who are you looking for?" said the stranger. Mary was crying so much she could not see the man, but she thought he must be the gardener.

"I'm looking for Jesus", she said. "Please, if you have moved his body, tell me where he is!"

Then the man said "Mary!" Mary looked up. It was Jesus! She was so happy she did not know what to do.

"Go and tell the others, Mary", said Jesus. "Tell them I am alive, and soon they will all see me again."

So Mary ran off with her wonderful news. And very soon, all Jesus' friends had seen him, and knew that he really was alive!

Christians today tell this story every year, at Easter. They are sad when they hear how Jesus was hurt and died. But when they hear how he came alive again, they laugh and sing happy songs, because they are sure that Jesus is still alive today, and although they cannot see him, they believe that he is there to help them every day of their lives.

Note:
Further information on the Easter festival can be found in the *Infant Teacher's Handbook*, pages 6 & 80, and in the *Junior Teacher's Handbook*, pages 7 & 97-101.

Holy Week, Easter and Whitsun

A Junior version

1. To Jerusalem

For three years Jesus had travelled round the countryside, teaching people, healing the sick, and showing people how God loves them. But gradually, some people began to turn against him. Some of the priests and teachers thought that he was teaching people to disobey the laws of their faith. Some of the Roman rulers thought that he was encouraging people to rebel against the power of Rome. And some people were simply jealous because the crowds loved Jesus.

So when Jesus set off on a journey to Jerusalem, he knew he was going into danger. He told his closest friends, his disciples, that he would be killed.

"God forbid!" said Peter. "You are God's anointed one, who will save our people! He will not let you be killed!"

Jesus looked at him reproachfully. "You do not understand, Peter. This is the way it must be. You only get in my way when you talk like that."

Peter looked helplessly at his friends. "Let us go to Jerusalem, then," he shrugged, "and die with him."

When they came near Jerusalem, word that Jesus was coming had spread before them, and there were thousands of people out to greet him. Jesus stopped and turned to two of the disciples.

"Go to the village over there," he said, "and bring me the donkey that you will find tethered there. If anyone stops you, just say that the master needs it and will return it soon."

So they went, and found the donkey as he had said, and brought it to Jesus. The disciples put their cloaks over the donkey's back, and Jesus mounted. And so it was that the people of Jerusalem, who had expected a great leader, maybe riding on a horse with hundreds of followers, saw instead a humble man riding on a donkey, with just his few friends walking behind him.

But the people of Jerusalem knew, nevertheless, that this was no ordinary man.

"Hosannah!" they shouted. "Hooray! Hosannah to the Son of David! Blessings on him who comes in the name of the Lord!"

And they took off their cloaks and laid them on the ground in front of Jesus. Some tore branches from the palm trees at the side of the road, and waved them like flags as Jesus came by.

Some of the teachers of the law tried to stop them. "Why can't you keep your followers under control?" they asked Jesus.

"I tell you," said Jesus, "if they did not shout out and greet me, then the very stones of the road would cry out in their place."

And so, with shouts and rejoicing, Jesus rode into Jerusalem.

2. The Plot

Jesus had been in Jerusalem some time, and the leaders of the people were getting more and more upset by him. He had spoken of how the humble would inherit the kingdom of God, not the learned teachers of the law. He had gone into the temple and seen the people buying and selling within the house of prayer. And he had taken a whip and turned them out. No one had ever seen him so angry before.

And still the crowds gathered round him. The leaders met together to decide what to do about Jesus.

"We could have him arrested", said one. "The Romans think he is a trouble maker, and would be glad to get him out of the way."

"But how?" asked another. "There are always crowds of people round him, and they all think he is a great prophet, or even the Messiah, God's chosen one. If he is arrested there will be a riot – and the Romans wouldn't thank us for that!"

Just then there was a knock at the door, and in walked a man they had seen before.

"Aren't you one of Jesus' disciples?" they asked.

"Yes, I am Judas Iscariot. I have been with Jesus from the beginning. What will you give me if I tell you how you can arrest him?"

For a moment the leaders were dumbfounded. They hurriedly consulted together in low voices. Then they said, "We will give you thirty silver coins. But it must be done quietly."

"Of course", said Judas. "I will come to you again when I know he is with just his friends. Then, when I take the soldiers to him, I will show them which one is Jesus by kissing him. Whoever I kiss, that's the man they must arrest."

And Judas went back to be with Jesus.

3. The Last Meal

It was festival time in Jerusalem – the Passover, when everyone sat down in their homes with friends and family for a special meal. But Jesus and his disciples had left their homes, and they were both friends and family to each other.

"Where shall we go to eat the Passover meal?" they asked him.

"Go into the city, and you will see a man carrying a pot of water. Follow him, and when he goes into a house, go in too, and say to the owner of the house, 'The Master says, where is the room where I can eat the Passover with my disciples?' He will show you a room upstairs, and that is where you are to make the preparations for our Passover meal."

They did this, and when all was ready, Jesus and his disciples came to the house. When they got there, the disciples looked round for the servant who would wash their feet, for in that hot and dusty country, it was the custom for a servant to wash the feet of anyone who came into the house. But before anyone else could move, Jesus took off his robe, which he wore for the festival, and wrapped a towel round himself. Then he filled a bowl with water, and knelt down by his disciples' feet. He began to wash their feet, and dry them with the towel round his waist. For a few moments they watched in silence. Then Jesus came to Simon Peter. Peter drew back.

"Lord," he said, "are you going to wash my feet?"

"At the moment", replied Jesus, "you do not know what I am doing. But later on you will understand."

But Peter was ashamed to have his beloved master serving him like a slave.

"No, Lord!" he cried. "You shall never wash my feet!"

Jesus looked at him. "If I do not wash you, you can never be part of me."

"In that case," cried Peter, never one to do anything by halves, "don't only wash my feet, but my hands and my head as well!"

"There is no need", smiled Jesus. "You are clean."

Then Jesus put on his robe again and they sat down to supper.

"Do you understand what I have done?" Jesus asked them. "I am your Lord, your teacher and your Master. If I have washed your feet – that is to teach you that you must wash each other's feet. Follow my example."

As they sat eating, Jesus looked round the table and sighed.

"I have wanted so much to eat this Passover meal with you before I suffer", he said. "For we will not eat together again until we celebrate together in God's kingdom. But I am sad, because one of you will betray me."

The disciples were horrified. "Not I, Lord, surely?" each one asked in a shocked voice.

"It is one of you who has dipped his bread into the same dish with me – one of my friends", answered Jesus.

Then Judas, not to be outdone, asked, "Not I, Lord, surely?"

Jesus looked at him. "Those are your words", he said quietly. And some time later, Judas slipped away.

Then they came to the part of the Passover meal where bread is broken and given to each person. Jesus took the bread, said the blessing over it, and gave some to each of them. "Eat this", he said. "This is my body which will be given for you. Do this to remember me."

Then he took a cup of wine and passed it among them. "This is my blood which will be poured out for you", he said. "Drink from it, all of you. Do this, whenever you meet, to remember me."

Then he went on to tell them how he would soon be arrested, and would die.

"And you," he said, "you will all leave me."

"Master," said Peter, "I will never leave you!"

"You will, Peter," replied Jesus, "but when all this is over, you will strengthen the others."

"No!" cried Peter. "If I have to go to prison, and even die, I will never leave you!"

Jesus looked at him. "I tell you Peter," he said, "before the cock crows tomorrow morning, you will have said three times that you do not know me."

4. Gethsemane

After supper the little group of friends left the house and went together to a garden, called Gethsemane, just outside the city. Jesus walked ahead, and the disciples followed, puzzled and afraid, for they could see that Jesus was deeply troubled.

"He says he is going to die," they thought, "but why does he not escape? God will surely save him from the soldiers! We have seen him heal the sick and even bring the dead to life. Will he not save himself?"

When they got to the garden, Jesus went a little way away to pray on his own. The disciples huddled together in the night. They tried to keep awake, and they tried to pray for the dark hours that lay ahead. But their eyes were heavy with grief.

Jesus, alone in the dark, was in turmoil. He didn't want to die. He knew what a cruel and barbarous death it would be.

"Father," he prayed, "if you are willing, take this cup away from me. Do not make me drink this suffering. But let it be as you wish, not as I wish."

But his agony did not go away. He prayed with even greater anguish. The disciples, watching from a distance, saw the sweat pouring from his face as he knelt there. And it seemed to them it was more like drops of blood falling from him. And then, as they watched their beloved master struggling with his feelings, they could see that he was not alone. All round him were angels, surrounding him, supporting him and comforting him. And, as their weary eyes closed in spite of themselves, the disciples knew that all that Jesus had told them would happen.

They did not know how long they slept but, all of a sudden, Jesus was there with them.

"Wake up!" he cried. "Get up and pray not to be put to the test!"

But already they could see that it was too late. Through the trees they could see the lanterns of the soldiers approaching, and heard their shouts. And then Judas was there with them. He went up to Jesus and said, "Master!" and kissed him. And, as the soldiers had been told, they seized hold of Jesus, tied him up, and led him away.

5. Peter's Denial

The soldiers took Jesus to the court of Caiaphas, the High Priest, and there, through the night, they questioned him. The High Priest was sure that Jesus had been teaching people against their religion, and saying disrespectful things about God. But no matter what the people said, and no matter what they accused him of, Jesus said nothing.

Meanwhile, Peter had followed. He had said that he would never leave Jesus, and he wasn't going to. He hung about with the crowd of soldiers and servants round the court of the High Priest, waiting to see what would happen. They had lit a fire, for the night was cold, and Peter mingled with the others, warming himself. Suddenly one of them turned to Peter, and said, "Haven't I seen you with this Jesus?"

"I don't know what you are talking about!" said Peter, before he stopped to think.

He moved away from the fire and stood near the gateway. He tried to look as if he was meant to be there, and began chatting with the servants. But suddenly one of them turned to him and said, "You were with Jesus!"

"No!" cried Peter. "I don't know the man!"

"Yes, surely," said another, "you talk with a Galilean accent. You're one of those with Jesus!"

Then Peter panicked and began to bluster. "I swear to you, I don't know him!" he said.

Just then the cock crowed, and Peter remembered what Jesus had said. In shame, he pushed his way through the crowd to the dark street outside. There he sat down and wept bitterly.

6. *The Trial*

The High Priest and his followers questioned Jesus all night. As dawn broke, they were more sure than ever that Jesus must die.

"He has spoken against all that we believe!" they cried.

But they did not have the power to put Jesus to death. For that they needed the Roman law and the Roman soldiers. So they sent him, still bound like a criminal, to the Roman governor, Pontius Pilate. On the way, the soldiers beat him with whips, and laughed at him. When they came to Pilate, they told him that Jesus had claimed to be king of the Jews. Pilate turned to Jesus.

"Is this true?" he asked.

"It is you who say it", replied Jesus.

"But don't you hear what they are saying about you?" asked Pilate. "If these things are true, I will have to condemn you to death!"

But Jesus said nothing.

Pilate knew that they could prove nothing against Jesus. But he also knew that the leaders who had brought Jesus to him were very powerful men, and could make a lot of trouble for him if he did not do what they wanted. He knew that there was a huge crowd outside, so he decided to play safe. He went out to talk to the crowd.

"People of Jerusalem!" he shouted. "You know that at this great festival time I always release one prisoner as a gesture of goodwill from your Roman rulers. Now, I have two prisoners at the moment. One is Barabbas, that famous terrorist and murderer. The other is Jesus. Which one shall I release?"

Pilate remembered how the people had greeted Jesus with such joy only a short time before. But to his astonishment they shouted, "Barabbas! Release Barabbas!"

"Then what should I do with Jesus?" asked Pilate.

The answer came back even louder, "Kill him! On a cross! Crucify him!"

Pilate felt trapped. He had asked the people, hoping that would save Jesus. Now he did not know what to do. He knew that as Roman governor, it was his decision. But he didn't want to decide. He sent for a bowl of water. In front of everyone he washed his hands.

"Watch this, all of you", he said. "You may crucify this man, but it is your decision. I have washed my hands, and that shows that I am not guilty of shedding his innocent blood."

Then he handed Jesus over to his soldiers, to do what they wanted with him.

7. *The Crucifixion*

The Roman soldiers jeered and mocked Jesus.

"He said he was a king!" they laughed. "Let's make a king out of him!"

So they put a purple robe on him, and put a reed in his hand for a sceptre.

"What about a crown?" one of them shouted. "He needs a crown!"

They plaited a crown out of sharp thorns, and pushed it onto his head so that his forehead bled. Then they knelt before him, laughing, and shouting, "Hail, King of the Jews!"

When they had finished their fun with him, they put his own robe on him again, made him carry the heavy cross on his shoulders, and led him out to be killed. They took him to a place outside the city, where crucifixions always took place. It was called Golgotha, which meant the place of the skull. There they nailed his hands and feet to the cross, and put it upright for him to die slowly and in great pain.

Jesus was not the only one to die on a cross that day, for it was the normal Roman punishment for crimes. On either side of Jesus there were robbers also being crucified. One of them looked bitterly at him.

"You called yourself a king", he said. "Look at you now! If you are the son of God as you say, why don't you save yourself, and us too?"

"Hold your tongue!" said the other robber. "Aren't you ashamed that this good man is receiving the same punishment as us? We are only paying the penalty for our crimes, but he's done nothing!" Then he turned to Jesus. "Jesus," he said, "remember me when you come into your kingdom."

"Indeed I will", said Jesus. "I tell you, this day you will be with me in Paradise."

There were many of Jesus's friends who gathered nearby to watch him die. Some of them could not believe that all they had hoped for, and the man they loved so much, had come to this. His mother was there too, watching helplessly as the hours went by, and her son slowly died.

When it was all over, and Jesus had died, his friends got permission from the Romans to take his body down from the cross. Gently and sadly they lifted him down, washed him, and wrapped him in a white cloth. Then they carried him to a tomb in a cave. They rolled a great stone across the mouth of the cave.

They could not anoint his body with fine oils, as was the custom of the time, because it was late – it would soon be the Sabbath, and their religion forbade them to work on the Sabbath. So, in deep sorrow, they left him.

8. *Easter Morning*

After the Sabbath was over, very early in the morning, three women, friends of Jesus, came to the tomb. They were bringing spices and ointments to put on the body to prepare it properly for burial.

"But the stone!" they said to each other as they approached the cave. "That great heavy stone over the mouth of the cave! Who will roll it away for us?"

But as they came closer to the cave they saw, to their astonishment, that the stone had already been rolled away from the mouth of the cave, and that the inside of the cave glowed brightly. They rushed into the cave to find two men in shining white clothes standing there.

"You are looking for Jesus of Nazareth", the men said. "He is not here but is risen. Go and tell his friends!"

And the women saw that there was no body lying in the cave. Full of wonder, and not knowing what to believe, they went away. But one of them, Mary Magdalene, stayed behind. She had not understood what the men said to them, she was still too full of grief for Jesus, whom she had loved more dearly than anyone she had ever known. All she knew was that he was dead, and even his body had disappeared. Blinded by tears, she wandered about the garden where the cave was.

"What's the matter? Who are you looking for?" asked a voice behind her. She looked round and saw a man she thought must be the gardener.

"They have taken Jesus away", she sobbed. "If you have moved him, please tell me where you have put him."

"Mary!" said the man.

As he said her name, Mary knew at once that it was Jesus.

"My Master!" she said, in joy and wonder. Jesus sent her to tell the others that he was alive.

9. *In the Upper Room*

Jesus' disciples heard what Mary and the other women had to say. But they could not believe it. They had seen Jesus die, they had themselves taken his body down from the cross and laid it in the tomb. How could he be alive again?

One evening some of the disciples were gathered together secretly in a room at the top of a house. They had to meet secretly because there were still many enemies of Jesus looking for them. So they met at night, and made sure that the doors were locked.

But suddenly, although they heard no sound and no one had opened the door, there was Jesus amongst them. At first they were terrified.

"Do not be frightened", said Jesus. "I am not a ghost. I am real, and alive. Look, have you anything to eat?"

They gave him a piece of fish, and he ate it before their eyes.

"It must be true!" they said to themselves. "Ghosts don't eat!" and they gathered round him joyfully. Jesus laid his hands on each one of them and said: "Peace be with you!", and then he was gone. But the disciples left behind sat gazing at each other, lost in happiness. Just then two more disciples came rushing into the room.

"He is alive!" they shouted. "We have seen him!" With excitement and wonder they told their story.

"We were walking to the village of Emmaus, and as we went we talked about Jesus. We went over and over what has happened in the last few days and, as we talked all our love and grief for Jesus came over us, and we could hardly keep from weeping there on the road. And someone came up to us and said, 'What is it you are talking about?' So we told him all about how we had thought that Jesus was the Messiah, God's chosen one, but he'd been killed, so we must have been wrong. And then he began to talk to us, and suddenly everything dropped into place. He talked about the prophets, and about God, and how it had been foretold that the Messiah must suffer, and everything he said seemed so right, it was as if our hearts were on fire within us. So, when we got to Emmaus, we said to him, 'Look, we are stopping here, and it's late in the day. Why don't you stop with us and have supper?' so he came in with us, and as soon as we sat down to supper, he took bread, and broke it for us, just as Jesus did that dreadful night. And as soon as he did that, we knew him. I don't know why we hadn't recognised him before, but in that moment, we knew that Jesus was alive. And at that moment, he left us. But we came straight back here to tell you the wonderful news!"

How the disciples rejoiced that night as they exchanged their stories! But one of them, Thomas, was not there. The next day, the other disciples rushed to tell him.

"No", said Thomas. "That can't be so. You have imagined it. The terrible things that have happened have made you think it is so, but people do not come back to life. I can't believe it. Unless I see the marks of the nails on his hands and feet, and put my hand on the wound in his side, I will not believe that Jesus is alive again."

That evening, the disciples all met together again, as they had done every evening since Jesus died. This time Thomas was with them. And again, Jesus appeared among them. Again they all gathered round. But Thomas hung back. "Thomas," said Jesus, "come here and touch my hands and feet. Put your hand into my side and feel the wound there that the soldier's spear made. Set your mind at rest, and believe!"

"No", said Thomas. "Now I have seen for myself. Now I do not need to touch you. I believe!"

"But come here, Thomas, and be certain", said Jesus. "I do not want you to have any doubt in future. You believe because you have seen with your own eyes. But those who believe what they have not seen are even happier."

10. Ascension and Pentecost

The good news spread amongst Jesus' disciples – "We have seen him. He is alive!" More and more of them met Jesus, and recognised him, and believed. Some of them were impatient for Jesus to show his power once more, to prove that he was the Son of God.

But he said to them: "God has a plan, and when the time is right, he will act. But you do not know when things are to happen. Before long I will leave you, and you will not see me any more. But don't do anything – just wait in Jerusalem. I will send the Holy Spirit to you – you will not see him, but you will become brave, and powerful, and you will carry on the work I have done here on earth. You will tell people about me, not only here in Jerusalem, but all over the world. Just wait for the Holy Spirit."

And while Jesus was speaking to them, they saw him lifted up from the earth towards heaven. They gazed upward, but a cloud came between them and Jesus, and they saw him no more. They were puzzled, they felt again a little lost without Jesus, but they knew by now that Jesus kept his promises, so, as he had told them, they stayed together in Jerusalem, praying together and waiting for the Holy Spirit who would show them what to do.

The days went by, and still they waited. Then one day, the day of the festival of Pentecost, they were all gathered together early in the morning, praying as usual. Suddenly they heard a sound like a rushing, mighty wind. The house shook, and the roaring filled their ears. Then they saw what looked like flames of fire. The fire split into separate flames, and came to rest on the head of each of them. Suddenly they knew what they had to do, and after all their hesitation and fears, it now seemed not only possible, but the only thing to do. They rushed into the street, full of happiness, and began to tell everyone about Jesus and about all that God had done for them and for all the people in the world.

Those who heard them were amazed. There were people in Jerusalem from many different countries, all come for the festival. They had all heard about the death of Jesus, and how his followers were living in hiding, afraid that they might be found and killed too. But here they were, shouting about Jesus in the middle of the street, saying that he had risen from the dead, that he was God's son, that everyone should follow him!

But it took a moment before they realised the most astonishing thing about what was going on.

"Wait!" said one of the passers by. "These men are from Galilee, and they've never had any education. I'm from Greece, and I only speak Greek. So how does it happen that I can understand what they're saying?"

"I'm from Egypt," said another, "and they're speaking my language too!"

"But I'm from Parthia", said another. "That's Parthian they're speaking!"

No one understood how it could be, but everyone who listened to what the disciples were saying, heard them speak in their own language.

But there were others who did not listen so carefully. "These people are just drunk!" they laughed.

And then came perhaps the most extraordinary moment of that extraordinary morning. For Peter stood up to speak to the people. Peter, the humble fisherman, who had followed Jesus for years but never seemed to understand what he said; Peter, who only a few weeks before had told people that he did not know Jesus; Peter, who had never spoken in public before in his life, stood up and spoke to that vast crowd. He told them that Jesus was the one that God had promised to his people, that Jesus was the one they had been waiting for all these years, and they had let him be killed.

"But God has brought him to life again!" cried Peter. "And it is not too late to turn to him, and follow him. He will give you the Holy Spirit that he has now given to us, and you too will know him and tell others about him!"

And so it was that, in that one morning, about three thousand people decided to follow Jesus, who had died and risen from the dead.

After that wonderful morning the disciples had many adventures and went through many dangers as they went about telling people about Jesus. Many of them were killed because they would not stop teaching about Jesus. But the message did not stop. Because those confused, hesitant and frightened people had changed. They no longer did things on their own, but always with the help of the Holy Spirit of Jesus, who promised to be with them always, even to the end of the world.

Note:
This story can be told in conjunction with work in the *Junior Teacher's Handbook*, pages 16, 17 & 30 (Peter's denial).

The Conversion of St. Paul

After his death and resurrection, Jesus stayed with his disciples for a short while then returned to heaven. When he had returned to heaven, his followers were persecuted by some of the Jews. One of Jesus' followers, a man called Stephen, had been stoned to death. Among the people who stood there when he was being stoned was a young man called Saul of Tarsus. Saul was a very religious man who believed that the followers of Jesus were teaching things which were wrong and against God.

Saul travelled to Damascus; he wanted to find followers of Jesus there to capture them and take them to Jerusalem. As he drew near to Damascus, suddenly a light shone from heaven and he fell on the ground. He heard a voice saying to him. "Saul, Saul, why are you persecuting me?"

So Saul said, "Who are you Lord?"

The voice replied, "I am Jesus whom you are persecuting. Rise and go into the city. You shall be told what to do."

The men who were travelling with him stood there terrified, because they could hear a voice, but see no one. Saul got up from the ground. When he opened his eyes, he could see nothing; he was blind. The men who were with him led him by the hand and took him into Damascus. He was there for three days, blind and not eating or drinking anything.

There was a disciple of Jesus at Damascus, whose name was Ananias. God appeared to him in a vision and said, "Arise and go to the street which is called Straight and ask in the house of Judas for one named Saul, a man of Tarsus. He is praying and he has seen a vision of a man named Ananias coming in and laying his hands on him, so that he may get his sight back."

Ananias knew that Saul had been persecuting Christians in Jerusalem and was going to capture any that he found in Damascus. He did not want to go to Judas' house, but God explained that Saul had a purpose to serve. Saul would teach not only Jews but also Gentiles (people who were not Jews) about Jesus.

So Ananias went to the house where Saul was and put his hands on him. He said, "Brother Saul the Lord, Jesus, who appeared to you on the way here, has sent me that you may get back your sight". Straightaway, something like scales fell from Saul's eyes and he could see again. He got up and was baptised to show that he too had become a follower of Jesus. He went on to become a great teacher and a leader of the new church. After he had become a follower of Jesus, he was known as Paul, and many letters which he wrote to Christians in different parts of the world can be found in the Christian holy book, the Bible.

Saint Lucy

On December 13th Swedish people celebrate the life and bravery of a young woman who lived many centuries ago in Italy. In Swedish and Italian she is called Saint Lucia. In English her name is Saint Lucy. Several different legends are told about her life. This is one of them.

Saint Lucy lived just three hundred years after the birth of Jesus – at a time when Rome was still a mighty empire. In fact this story starts not with Saint Lucy herself, but with the Roman Emperor Diocletian.

Now Diocletian wanted to make the empire strong and great so that no one could ever harm it. He strengthened his armed forces throughout the land. He ordered the building of bridges, viaducts, storehouses, and meeting places. Some of them still stand even today. He wanted everyone to be proud of belonging to his empire and he wanted them all to share the same religion – the old Roman religion which encouraged the worship of the old gods such as Jupiter, Apollo and Mars. It was a religion in which Rome and the Emperor were honoured and glorified.

So Diocletian ordered all of his subjects to show their loyalty by worshipping at the shrines he set up, and he outlawed all other religions.

"Are all my people obeying my laws?" he asked his generals when they came to report to him news of the empire.

"The temples are full", they replied.

"But are all my people visiting the shrines? Are all my people obeying me?" he asked again.

"Er – not all-" came the answer. "The Christians will not go. They refuse to obey you. They say they will only worship their God and his son Jesus."

Diocletian was very angry that anyone should dare to disobey his command. He was angry too because he saw the Christians as a threat to the peace of the Roman Empire. In his fury he ordered that all the Christians be rounded up and put to death unless they renounced their faith.

Throughout the land soldiers set about their grim task of seeking out the Christians and throwing them in gaol ready for execution. Sometimes it was easy to find Christians, at other times it was harder. They had to listen to rumours of Christians meeting together to remember the Lord Jesus. They had to rely on spiteful folk who were willing to betray their neighbours.

Outside some of the towns and cities in Italy were secret networks of underground tunnels, called catacombs, which were only known to the Christians. This was where they buried their dead, laying the bodies out on tiered ledges at the side of the tunnels. In previous persecutions these catacombs had made good hiding places, and it was to them now that many Christians once more fled. They bundled together food and blankets, and crept out of the city when the night was darkest, to live like moles in the depths of the earth. Whole families sought shelter this way, trusting that the persecution would be short-lived, and that they would soon be able to return to their every-day lives.

In the city of Syracuse, however, one young Christian woman called Lucy, did not flee. Although she believed in Jesus, her family were not Christian and she seemed to be in no danger. She knew of those who had gone into hiding and they were constantly in her thoughts and prayers. She imagined them huddled together for warmth, trying to get comfortable on the hard stone slabs, but cheering each other up by singing hymns that would echo down the long tunnels. She thought of them rocking the crying babies to sleep in their arms, and how they would probably be telling over and over again the stories of Jesus. Lucy prayed and prayed for them, asking that God would meet their needs, and as she prayed she realized that one of their needs must be for food.

"Please let someone take them food", she prayed. "Please, dear Lord, please."

Slowly she began to realize that she could be the answer to her own prayers. She could take food to those in hiding!

She lay awake that first night making plans. She knew where she could get food. She knew of a path that would take her to the catacombs without anyone noticing her. But then there were the catacombs themselves! Lucy shuddered when she thought of those tunnels. They would be pitch black and to find the living she would have to walk between the bodies of the dead. Who knows what awful creatures would be on the floor, spiders maybe or snakes, and she might trip over rocks. She would have to take plenty of candles of course – more than one – it wouldn't be so frightening if she could see properly. But how could she carry the candles – she would have her hands full of food. What was she to do? Suddenly she had an idea. She could carry them on her head! She could make a crown to hold them.

The next night Lucy slipped out of the house with as much food as she could carry and, with only the light of the stars to guide her, she made her way to the catacombs. At the entrance she placed the candle crown gingerly on her head, and warily began her precarious walk into the total darkness. She tried not to think of the skeletons, she tried not to think of the spiders and the rats and snakes. She just looked at the path ahead and prayed hard, very hard, for courage.

Imagine the surprise of the fugitives when they saw emerging from the black, a white-clad figure, her head surrounded by a halo of light. They must have thought she was an angel sent from God. Imagine their delight and relief when they saw she had food for them.

Night after night Lucy visited the catacombs and she was always a welcome visitor. With each trip her courage grew. She no longer felt so afraid, but she still continued to wear her crown of light.

But she had another problem, for she was not only brave but beautiful. A wealthy man in the town saw her, fell in love with her and sought to make her his wife.

"Say yes", her father told her. "He has lots of money. He will make you a fine husband, and you will have an important place in our society."

But Lucy would not say yes. How could she? Her suitor worshipped the old gods. He would have shrines to them in his house.

She was a Christian, and she couldn't worship in a house full of shrines to Roman gods! Besides she must continue her secret missions to the catacombs. No, no she couldn't possibly marry him.

Her suitor begged and pleaded with her. He promised her fine clothes, and beautiful jewellery. He promised her slaves to wait on her every need. But the more he persisted the stronger her resolve become. She would not, could not, marry him.

At last he became angry, all his passionate love turned to bitterness and hate. If he couldn't have Lucy, then no one could. He went to the Roman authorities and denounced Lucy as a Christian, a traitor to the state.

Soldiers came and took Lucy away, and she was put to death under Roman law.

Ten years later Constantine was emperor of Rome. Unlike the emperors before him, Constantine liked the Christians, and gave protection to them. Now they could meet openly and build churches in which to worship together. And when they came together they remembered those who had died for the faith during the persecution and told their stories. The Christians in Syracuse told of Lucy, and how her name well suited her, for it means light and she brought light – the light of her candles and the light of her love, compassion and bravery to them while they hid in the catacombs.

Lucy's story spread throughout Christendom until it reached the far northern country of Sweden. There the winter days are short, and the sun is shrouded in mist. The people long for the light to return. The story of Saint Lucy bringing light made them think of their own longing for light and so they began to celebrate her day. That was in the time of the Vikings, but still today Swedish families follow the old custom. In each family, one of the daughters gets up very, very early and dresses in a long white gown and ties a red sash round her waist. Then she puts on her crown of lights, a wreath of greenery with seven candles in it (today the candles are often artificial battery-operated ones). She serves the family in bed with special buns and coffee. Sons in the family sometimes dress as stars in long shirts and pointed hats. They 'guide' Lucy up the stairs, as the stars guided Lucy to the catacombs so long ago.

Saint Christopher

There was once a giant of a man called Christopher. Christopher had decided that he would spend his life in service of only the mightiest of masters. But again and again he had been disappointed. He had tried serving the king, but was disappointed. He had even tried serving Satan, the evil one, but was disappointed. Just when he believed he had found a master worthy of service, he would be disappointed. Finally, in sadness he set up home by the ford of a river. There he helped travellers across by carrying them on his great shoulders.

Then, one stormy night, a small child came to him and asked to be carried across. "The wind blows a gale and the river is rough," said Christopher, "and you are too young to be out all alone." But the child persisted until at last Christopher agreed.

He put the child on to his shoulders and stepped into the water. At first the load was light, but, as he crossed the river, the child seemed to grow heavier and heavier and heavier. Christopher found himself staggering in the water, buffeted by the waves. He thought he would never make it across, he thought he would sink, but still for the sake of the child he battled on. At long last he reached the other side and set the child down.

He looked at the child in wonder and amazement. "Who are you?" he asked. The child stretched out his hands, and it was then that Christopher saw the cruel marks of nails in his hands and feet. "And who has dared to do this to you?" Christopher roared in anger.

The child replied: "You have been searching for the mightiest of masters. I am the one you seek, the King of Kings, Jesus Christ. I bear in my body the weight of the suffering of the world. Now you too have carried that weight."

From that day on, Christopher followed Jesus. Indeed his name means 'the bearer of Christ'. He became known as Saint Christopher, and many travellers today still ask Saint Christopher to guide and protect them on their journeys. Many of them carry with them a medallion with a picture of Saint Christopher on it.

Saint Francis

A long time ago in the country of Italy, there lived a young man whose name was Francis. He lived in a town called Assisi, and he had everything he could possibly want. His father had lots of money, and he had lots of friends. He didn't have to work hard, and he spent his days singing and playing and having fun. His father gave him plenty of money, and he spent it on fine clothes and good food.

He didn't mean to be unkind, and he would always help his friends if they needed anything, but he was so happy himself that he didn't want to see other people who were poor or ill or unhappy. If a beggar asked him for money, he might throw him a small coin without looking, but he did not want to see how poor and sad the person was. He never went near anyone who was ill, because they didn't look very nice, and it made him feel ill to look at them.

In those days there were many people who suffered from an illness called leprosy. Leprosy makes the skin look very nasty, and as the illness gets worse, people cannot use their hands or feet properly. Nowadays it can be cured, although there are still people who suffer from it. But in those days there was no cure, so lepers (people with leprosy) were sent to live with other lepers, away from healthy people, because healthy people were afraid that they would catch leprosy from them. Francis particularly hated so see lepers, and if he saw a leper by the side of the road, he would jump on his horse and ride away as fast as he could.

But then, little by little, Francis began to change. It began when he himself became ill, a long way from home. That made him think. When he returned home, his friends were glad to see him, and they wanted him to come out and have fun with them, as he had before. But Francis was different. He still went out with his friends, but he didn't seem to have such a good time. He thought more about people who were poor and ill. And he spent a lot of time praying in a quiet place.

And as he prayed, he remembered more and more about Jesus. He remembered that Jesus had loved poor people, and had talked with them a lot. He remembered that Jesus had helped sick people, and had told his friends to do the same.

So Francis began to try to do the same as Jesus. When his father gave him money, he gave it to poor people, instead of spending it on clothes for himself. And he began to visit people who had leprosy. He didn't just take them money or medicine and leave it at their house. He went right in, and he looked after the people as if he had been their servant. He washed their dirty bodies when they were too ill to wash themselves, and he put bandages on their sore skin. When they could not use their hands to eat he fed them and, when they could not walk he carried them where they wanted to go.

After a little while, Francis decided that even this was not enough. It was no good him trying to help poor people when he was so rich. He decided that God wanted him to become poor too. So he gave back to his father everything that his father had given him – all his fine clothes, his horses, and his money. He put on a plain brown cloak, and he set off into the world to tell everyone how Jesus loves poor people, and those who are sick or unhappy.

People tell many stories about Francis. They tell how he loved to laugh and play. They tell how he loved people who were not very clever, or who made silly mistakes. And they tell how he loved animals, just because God made them.

Since that time many people have done what Francis did. They too have given up all the things they own, and have spent their time helping the sick and telling people about Jesus. Many of them still today wear a simple brown cloak, just like Francis. Because they do what Francis did, they are called Franciscans.

Note:
This story can be told in conjunction with work in the *Junior Teacher's Handbook*, page 11 and with work on 'Who should we honour?' in the *Junior Assembly Book*, page 55.

Bernadette of Lourdes

*Christians often visit places where they believe Jesus or his mother
Mary have appeared to people for a special purpose. A very famous
place of pilgrimage is Lourdes, in France.*

About a hundred and fifty years ago, there was a young
peasant girl called Bernadette who lived near Lourdes, in
France. She was in poor health, and could not play with
other children very easily, so she spent much time on her own.

Then, one day, when she was out collecting firewood, she wandered into a small cave. Suddenly she stopped and stared, for she
realised that she was not alone. A beautiful lady was standing in
the cave, dressed in shining white clothes. Bernadette knew at
once that this was no ordinary lady, but someone special, and she
fell to her knees in prayer. "Hail, Mary, full of grace", she whispered. "Blessed mother of our Lord Jesus Christ." She closed her
eyes, for she was dazzled by the brightness of Mary's face. When
she opened them again, there was no one there. Had she imagined
it? Slowly Bernadette got to her feet and returned home. She
didn't tell anyone what she had seen – it was too wonderful, too
precious and too strange. But she could not keep away from the
little cave in the woods where she had seen Mary. Day after day
she returned there. And before long she saw Mary again, just as
before, in the grotto.

Bernadette did not know why she should have been chosen to
see this wonderful thing. She had never done anything special,
she was not clever. But she loved God with all her heart. This time
when she saw Mary, she was too excited to keep it to herself. She
whispered it to her mother, and to the parish priest. Soon the word
spread.

"Bernadette's been seeing visions!"

"Do you think she's going mad?"

"Maybe that illness of hers is affecting her brain."

"No, she's only making it up to get attention."

"She is there!" said Bernadette. "Come and see!"

So the people went with Bernadette to the cave. They saw
Bernadette's face light up with joy as they came near the place, and
they saw her fall to her knees in prayer. They saw her speak, and

listen as if for an answer. But as far as they could see she was talking to thin air!

"Now we know she's mad!" they said, and left her.

Some people laughed at Bernadette, some tried to be kind, and make allowances for her. All of them tried to persuade her that she had not seen anything. But Bernadette went on seeing the beautiful lady whom she knew to be the mother of Jesus.

One day the lady told Bernadette, "Wash yourself in the spring and drink from it." Bernadette looked round. The only water in the grotto was a muddy trickle. Obediently, Bernadette bent down and drank from it, and smeared her face in the mud, as if she were washing.

"There you are, you see", said the people watching her. "She's mad. What more proof do you need?"

But the next day, the priest visited the grotto early in the morning, and came back puzzled.

"That muddy puddle", he said, "has become a clear spring. There's cold, pure water bubbling up from it and flowing down the hill. Maybe she did see something, after all."

The story of the spring, and how it had sprung up overnight, spread throughout the country. People came to see it, to drink from it and wash in it. And that was how they realised how very special it was. Sick people who bathed in the water were suddenly cured of their illnesses!

That spring has been flowing ever since, very cold, very clear, and very pure. The fame of the water at Lourdes has spread all round the world. Today thousands of people travel to Lourdes each year to give honour to Mary. Many of them are ill or disabled and they bathe in the waters hoping to be cured. Some are cured and many more believe that Mary, the mother of Jesus, has helped them. They feel her presence there, and go back to their homes with new strength and new hope.

Note:
This story can be told in conjunction with work on 'What happens on pilgrimage', pages 74 & 75, in the *Junior Teacher's Handbook*.

Tales from the Hindus

How Can a Demon be Killed?

Hindus believe that there is good and bad in everything, but that sometimes the bad becomes so powerful that it takes over. It is then that the great god Vishnu comes into the world to restore the balance between good and bad. Hindus tell of ten such occasions when Vishnu came into the world. On each occasion he took a different shape – sometimes human, sometimes animal. These are known as the Ten Avatars of Vishnu. This story is about the Avatar Narasimha, the Lion Man.

At one time the world was ruled by a terrible demon. He was fierce, cruel and arrogant, and not even the gods knew how to defeat him. For long ago the demon had been told:

"You will never be killed by god, man or animal."

"You need never fear death in the day or at night."

"No weapon will be able to kill you."

"You cannot be destroyed on earth or in the heavens."

"You can never be killed either indoors or out-of-doors."

With this promise, the demon believed that no one could ever defeat him, and his arrogance grew day by day. In particular, he enjoyed torturing those who tried to be faithful to Lord Vishnu, and to live a good life. He even attacked his own son Prahlad when Prahlad became a follower of Lord Vishnu. But Vishnu protected Prahlad and the demon could not harm him.

As time passed, the demon became so cruel that eventually the whole of creation cried out to Vishnu to help them escape from the demon's evil rule. The demon's attack on Prahlad had made Vishnu angry, and now he determined to destroy the demon. But how can you kill a demon who cannot be harmed by god, man or animal; neither by day or night; neither on earth nor in heaven; not with any weapon; neither indoors nor out-of-doors?

One day the demon was tormenting the faithful Prahlad. It was dusk, and therefore neither day nor night. The demon was annoyed that he had not been able to harm Prahlad.

"Tell me," he said, "where do you get your strength from?"

"From the same source that you and all other creatures get their strength", replied Prahlad. "From Lord Vishnu, of course."

"Where is this Vishnu?" roared the demon. "I'm sick of hearing about him! Where is he? I want to kill him!"

"He is everywhere!" Prahlad replied.

"Is he in this stone pillar?"

"Why, of course."

The demon drew his sword and rushed at the pillar. With a roar, he smashed his sword into it as hard as he could. Immediately there was an answering roar like rushing wind, and a crashing noise. From inside the pillar itself, Vishnu appeared in his most terrifying form. He had the head of a great lion, the body of a man and the claws of a fierce hunting lion. So he was not god, man nor animal. Vishnu leapt upon the demon and carried him to the doorway, so that he was neither indoors nor out. Lifting the demon on to his knees, Vishnu tore the wicked demon in two, destroying him neither on earth nor in the heavens, and using no weapon.

With the death of the demon, evil retreated once again into the shadows and the whole earth praised Lord Vishnu, the Preserver.

Note:
Further information on the Avatars of Lord Vishnu can be found in the *Infant Teacher's Handbook*, page 81 and in the *Junior Teacher's Handbook* page 113.

The Birth of Krishna

*Janmashtami is the festival which celebrates the birth of the god
Krishna. In India, during Janmashtami, hundreds of thousands of
pilgrims travel from all over the country to Vrindaban, where Krishna
was born. All day the pilgrims fast, waiting for midnight, the hour of
Krishna's birth. Then, as midnight comes, the air is filled with the
ringing of temple bells and the sounds of priests blowing on conch
shells. In the temple, a statue of the baby Krishna is put into a
beautifully decorated swing. Pilgrims flock from one temple to another
to rock the swing and pray that Krishna will help them. There is
feasting and dancing, and actors tour the streets telling stories. This is
one of the stories they tell of how Krishna was born.*

Long, long ago, a demon came and ruled the earth. His name
was Kamsa. He was evil and struck fear into all who saw
him.

Then one day Kamsa heard a voice from heaven.

"Beware!" said the voice. "Your sister's eighth son will kill
you!"

So Kamsa decided to make sure that this could never happen.
He only had one sister, and her name was Devaki. He seized
Devaki and her husband, and threw them into a deep dungeon
and locked the doors. There in the dungeon Devaki gave birth to
seven children. Kamsa killed them all.

Then Devaki became pregnant again. She gave birth to the baby
Krishna, who was the god Vishnu in human form. At midnight,
just as Krishna was born, the doors of the prison sprang open and
the guards fell asleep. Devaki's husband gathered the baby up in
his arms and fled with him to the forest of Vraj, where he exchanged the baby Krishna for a girl who had just been born to a
woman called Yasoda. Yasoda was fast asleep, and when she
woke up she thought she had given birth to a boy.

Meanwhile Devaki's husband placed the baby girl in Krishna's
empty cradle in the dungeon. When Kamsa learnt that Devaki had
had her baby he rushed in to kill it. He grabbed the child but she
flew up into the air – she was really a goddess! Scornfully Devaki
told Kamsa that he had been tricked.

And so it was that Krishna grew up in the village and loved

Yasoda as his mother. She and her husband were good people who kept cows. Krishna played with the other children, and helped to look after the cows. He grew strong and beautiful and happy, and everyone loved him.

Note:
Further information on Janmashtami can be found in the *Infant Teacher's Handbook*, pages 7, 49 & 84 and in the *Junior Teacher's Handbook*, pages 8 & 117.

Krishna and the Butter

At Janmashtami, when Hindus celebrate the birth of Krishna, groups of boys stand on each others' shoulders to form pyramids. They try to reach clay pots full of milk and rice which people hang from high windows. This is a reminder of one of the stories which people tell about Krishna when he was a small boy.

The child Krishna lived in a village in India. The people in the village kept many cows, and every day each family would milk its cows and use the milk for food. Some of the milk they drank, some they made into yoghurt, and some they made into butter. They kept the butter and yoghurt in large clay pots.

Krishna was very fond of eating butter, so every day he watched as his mother Yasoda put the butter into the pots and put it away. Then, when her back was turned, he would dip his hand into the pot and steal some butter to eat. Mother Yasoda tried everything. She tried telling him off, she tried hiding the pots. But whatever she did, Krishna went on taking the butter. When he couldn't find butter to steal in his own house, he went to the neighbours and dipped his hand into their butter pots.

"I'll deal with you, young Krishna!" shouted the neighbours as they chased him down the village street. But every time they caught him, Krishna was such a lovable child, and gave them such a beautiful smile, that they couldn't punish him!

Then one day, Yasoda thought that she had found a way to stop Krishna from taking her butter once and for all. She got a rope and tied it to the butter pot. Then she reached up and tied the rope to the roof of her house, and pulled the butter up out of Krishna's reach.

But was it safe? No it was not. Krishna had a brother, Balarama, who was almost the same age as him, and he called Balarama to join in his mischief.

"You stand there Balarama," he said, "and let me climb on your shoulders." Then he took a stone, climbed on Balarama's shoulders, and broke the pot to get at the butter inside. What a feast the two boys had! They ate and ate until they were both full, and neither of them could manage another mouthful.

"But there is a lot more butter here", said Balarama. "Now we have taken it, it would be a shame to waste it. What shall we do?"

Krishna looked out of the house. "Look!" he cried. "My friends the monkeys! They have often played with me and brought me fruit from the tree-tops. Now I will give them something. Monkeys! Monkeys! Come here and share my butter!" Before long there was nothing to be seen of the butter but a lot of greasy paw marks and the broken pieces of the pot.

When Mother Yasoda found out, she was very, very angry.

"I have put up with Krishna's tricks up to now, because I love him dearly", she said. "But this is too much! I have to punish him!"

But first she had to catch him. Round and round the courtyard they ran, Yasoda very angry, and Krishna running away in fear. At last, Yasoda caught him.

"What am I going to do with you?" she cried. "I know, I'll tie you up. That will teach you what happens to people who steal!"

So she fetched a piece of rope and tried to tie it round Krishna. But it was not quite long enough. She fetched another piece, and joined it on. Still the rope would not go round Krishna. It was just a few centimetres too short. She fetched more rope, and then more, but each time there was not quite enough rope to tie Krishna up. At last she fetched all the rope she had in the house, joined it all together, and tried to tie it round Krishna. But still it was just a few centimetres too short.

At last Yasoda sat down and cried. She knew she had to punish her son for stealing, but she couldn't manage it! Why had everything gone wrong?

When Krishna saw her crying, he felt sorry for her. "Don't cry, mother", he said. "It's not your fault you can't tie me up. I know you love me, and I love you. So now I will sit still and take my punishment. Tie the rope round me."

So Yasoda took the rope, and tied it round Krishna. And this time, to her surprise, she found the rope went round him easily, with some to spare!

Hindus who tell this story explain why Yasoda could not tie Krishna up. For he was not an ordinary child, but God in human form. Of course no one can tie God up! No rope can reach round God. But because Yasoda loved him, and because he loved her, he let himself be tied up by the rope of love.

Note:
This story can be told in conjunction with work on 'Holi' in the *Junior Assembly Book*, page 11.

"Open Your Mouth!"

K rishna and his brother Balarama often went out to play in the forest with the other children in the village. They played all sorts of games: running, climbing trees; and piggy-back fighting.

Krishna was the leader of one team, and Balarama was the leader of the other. And, of course, sometimes their games turned into arguments, and they would run to their mother Yasoda, and each one would try to get the other into trouble.

One day they came running back from the forest after another argument.

"Mother, Mother!" shouted Balarama. "Do you know what he did? He's been eating dirt from the ground!"

"Krishna!" said Mother Yasoda. "Is this true?"

"No," said Krishna, "it's a lie!"

"Come here, my son", she said. "Come into the light, where I can see you. Now, open your mouth, and let me look."

So Krishna stood in the sunshine, and opened his mouth as wide as it would go. Yasoda looked into his mouth. And this is what she saw: she saw the earth and the sky, and everything that has ever been or ever will be. She saw the sun and the moon and the stars and the planets. She saw the four things that make up the universe – earth, water, fire and air. She saw the ocean and their own land of India, and the forest and the village. And she saw herself, Yasoda, with her son Krishna on her knee, and she was feeding him.

She felt as if her head was spinning, and she thought she was going to faint.

"What is happening?" she cried. "Am I going mad? It is as if I am looking into the mouth of God. But isn't this my own son Krishna, whom I love? What shall I do? I'm frightened!"

So Krishna closed his mouth so that she would not see any more. And, just as she had seen when she looked in his mouth, he sat on her knee, and she fed him. Yasoda hugged him, and knew that he was truly her own son Krishna, whom she loved.

But Hindus know that he was also God. When people see God too closely, they become frightened. So Krishna becomes for everyone a little child, or a brother, or a friend, so that they can love him and not be frightened.

The Story of the Ramayana

This is a story about Prince Rama, the great warrior, who was married to the beautiful Sita. Rama and Sita were really the god Vishnu and his wife Lakshmi in human form.

Prince Rama was heir to a great kingdom, but his stepmother had tricked his father into banishing him into the forest. With him went his wife, Sita, and his half-brother, Lakshmana.

Rama had begged Sita to stay safely in the palace while he was in exile, but she declared it was a thousand times better to be in the forest with Rama than in the richest palace without him.

Rama's loyal half-brother Lakshmana also refused to stay behind. He was almost exactly the same age as Rama, and the two had grown up together.

So the three of them went to live in the forest together. They lived a simple, peaceful life in a small cottage, learning how to worship from the holy men who lived in the forest.

But, before long, their peace was disturbed. A female demon saw Rama and wanted to marry him. She made herself look like a beautiful girl, and tried to get Rama to leave Sita. But when Rama took no notice of her, out of sheer envy she attacked Sita. Lakshmana could see that she was a demon, and he cut off her nose and ears. In rage, the demoness turned to her brother for help.

Now, her brother was the most terrible demon of all, the demon king Ravana, who lived on the island of Lanka. Ravana had twenty arms and ten heads, with eyes as red as coal fires and a mouthful of yellow fangs. When Ravana heard about the three exiles, and about Sita's beauty, he came up with a plan to have her for himself.

One day, when the three exiles were walking in the forest, they saw the most beautiful deer you can imagine. Its golden hide was as bright as the sun, its silver antlers as bright as the moon, its hooves shone as black as night, and its eyes were as blue as sapphires.

So delighted was Sita when she saw the deer that she begged Rama to catch it for her. Lakshmana was worried that this was some demon trick to try and split them up, but Sita pleaded with Rama, until he agreed to try and catch the deer for her. However, just to be sure that Sita was safe, he told Lakshmana to stay with her until he came back with the deer.

Sita and Lakshmana waited and waited for Rama to return and then just as they were beginning to worry, they heard Rama's voice cry, "Lakshmana... help me!"

"Go quickly, Lakshmana", said Sita. Lakshmana did not want to leave her alone, but Sita turned on him in fury and accused him of not caring for Rama. So off Lakshmana ran to find Rama.

As soon as Sita was alone, the demon Ravana swooped down and swept Sita up into his chariot pulled by winged fiends. Sita hid her eyes at the sight of the terrible king, and even the flowers sank into the ground with fright. The deer had been a demon in disguise sent by Ravana – the voice of Rama just an illusion. Both were tricks to ensure Sita would be left alone and unprotected.

As the chariot soared through the sky, the ancient king of the vultures heard Sita's cries and called to the demon to release her.

When Ravana only laughed, the brave old vulture attacked the demon king. His mighty talons destroyed the fiendish chariot and ripped off Ravana's ten left arms. But these grew back instantly and struck out at the vulture king with their ten swords. The noble bird fell to the ground, dying, and Ravana flew on with Sita under his arms. Despite her terror Sita thought quickly and scattered her jewellery piece by piece – first her golden anklets, then her ear-rings, then her glittering scarf – as a trail for Rama to follow. Far below a white monkey looked up and, seeing the glittering jewelry, thought the stars were falling.

It was a long time before Lakshmana found Rama beside the dead demon, who had been made to look like the beautiful deer. Realising that they had been tricked the two brothers ran back to their cottage as fast as they could, their hearts filled with dread. Finding Sita gone, they searched frantically until they came upon the vulture king. With his dying words the vulture told them what had happened, and showed them the direction that the demon Ravana had taken Sita.

It wasn't long before they found the trail of jewellery that Sita had left. They followed this until they met Hanuman, the white monkey, who had seen Sita's jewellery fall. Hanuman was a very special monkey because he was the son of the wind god. Hanuman took the brothers to the monkey city, that lay under the hills in a giant cavern. All the monkeys of the city were called to the marble square in the centre of the city, and messages were sent out to monkeys all over the world. They came in their millions from the woods and caves, and with them came their friends the bears. Twenty-three million animals filled the city and covered the hills like a great shaggy sea. After they had heard what had happened, they spread out to search the world for Sita.

It was the monkey, Hanuman, who came at last to the demon island of Lanka, where Sita was now a captive. The monkeys and bears with him stared in despair at the giant crashing waves that surrounded the island, but Hanuman, the son of the wind god, climbed to the highest hill, took a mighty breath and leapt into the clouds, and over the crashing waves. He landed in Lanka and quickly found Sita in a grove of trees near the palace. There she sat refusing to marry the evil Ravana.

Sita was overjoyed when she found out who Hanuman was and

she gave him a pearl from her hair to take to Rama. Then, Hanuman bounded away to fetch Rama and Lakshmana, and the great army of monkeys and bears.

But still the giant ocean waves kept Rama and his army away from the island. In frustration Rama cursed the ocean that kept them from Sita. But the Ocean said his heart was as vast as his waters, and he would keep afloat anything they laid upon him. And so the army began to build a bridge of rocks and grass and sand.

The squirrels came running out of the woods to help, every animal – large and small – contributed to the building, and soon the bridge stretched one hundred leagues to the island, and the animals poured across their bridge.

Long and terrible was the battle, as the animals fought the evil demons. Many great deeds were done, until at last Rama faced the demon Ravana on the battlefield. With his arrows Rama struck again and again at the heads of Ravana but, each time he chopped one off, a new one grew.

Then Rama took up his special bow and arrow that had been made by the sky god. He chanted a fire mantra, and his golden arrows blazed as they shot toward Ravana. But Ravana chanted a rain mantra so the clouds flocked into the skies and drenched the fire arrows with their rain. Then Rama spoke a wind mantra and the seven winds swept across the sky, blowing the rain-clouds beyond the horizon. Once more Rama put an arrow to his bow and shot. The wind and fire gods flew with it as it pierced Ravana's breast in a blinding flash. Ravana fell dead in an instant.

All the world rejoiced. The reign of the demons was over and Rama and Sita returned to their own country to rule. In celebration the gods showered flowers from the sky, and the people lined the streets with flags and garlands. In every home, an oil lamp was put in the window to welcome back the three exiles and their great army. And Rama and Sita ruled happily for many years until it was time for them to leave their life on earth and return to heaven.

Note:
This story can be told in conjunction with work in the *Infant Assembly Book*, page 13.

The Magic Herb Mountain

The epic poem of the Ramayana tells of the battle between Prince Rama and the demon king Ravana. The poem is very long and contains many details of the battle, each of which make a story in their own right. This is one of them, and it happened in the middle of the battle against Ravana.

When Rama's army of monkeys and bears had slain almost all the demon army, Indrajit, the demon king's son rode invisibly into the battle. Indrajit had prayed and made offerings to the gods so that he and his winged chariot were invisible to all but the gods.

Invisibly he circled the battle field – his arrows falling like a rain of fire on Rama's army below. Soon monkeys and bears lay dead and dying for as far as the eye could see. When it seemed that all were dead, Indrajit returned to the island of Lanka. But Hanuman the monkey had been promised by the gods that he would live until he chose to die. Although he was wounded in a hundred places, Hanuman searched the battlefield. Rama and Lakshmana lay unmoving, and Hanuman hung his head as the tears rolled down his furry cheeks. Then nearby he heard the hoarse whisper of Jambavan, the bear king, who was sorely wounded.

Jambavan told Hanuman to fly, like his father the wind, to the medicine mountain in the Himalayas. There he would find herbs growing on the steep sides that came from the moon and could heal all ills.

Hanuman leapt away like a blazing silver comet, over the sea and land until he saw the shining mountain. Every plant and herb glistened with the light of the moon that filled their leaves.

Impatient to return and unsure which herbs to choose, Hanuman lifted the whole mountain onto his shoulders and flew back. As he hovered above the field of bodies, wondering where to put the mountain, the healing fragrances of the herbs filled the air.

Below the creatures began to stir. Rama and Lakshmana lifted their heads. Soon the land was covered with monkeys and bears and people hugging each other and laughing in delight. Rama's army was ready for battle once more.

Sita in the Fire

This is another story from the epic poem of the Ramayana.
After Prince Rama had killed the demon king Ravana, Hanuman the
monkey god flew to the grove where Sita had been kept captive by
Ravana.

"Dearest Sita, your Lord Rama has defeated the evil Ravana, and now he wants only to have you by his side once again", said Hanuman, his white furry face all crinkled with happiness.

"Oh Hanuman, I can hardly wait to see him again", said Sita.

Hanuman thought to himself that no jewels had ever shone as brightly as Sita's eyes. Then he remembered the jewellery that he saw falling like stars as Ravana flew across the sky with Sita. The jewellery was still tucked in the pocket of his white velvet cloak. He gave it to Sita, saying, "You shine brighter than the brightest gold." Sita put on the anklets and earrings and put the diamond pins in her hair. Then the two hurried to the battle-field where everyone was waiting for Sita.

A great cheer went up as she appeared. Flags waved and monkeys and bears danced about and threw blossoms at her feet. Rama stood motionless in the middle of the field, looking at the one he loved more than anything in the world. Her black hair sparkled with the diamonds, like the sky at midnight, and her eyes were as large as lotus flowers. She was so beautiful and her face so kind and loving that Rama could not bear to think someone else might have her love. Suddenly he was filled with fear. Perhaps Sita's heart was no longer pure in its devotion to him? Perhaps she had come to love Ravana while she stayed at his palace? She was so loving that she would forgive even a demon who kidnapped her.

Now Rama felt like crying. He was sure Sita loved Ravana. Sita walked towards him, looking a little puzzled as she saw the darkness settle on his face. The cheering went quiet as the monkeys and bears noticed it too.

"Rama?" said Sita.

"I'm sorry," said Rama, "you cannot come back to me, now that you have lived in another man's house. How can I know you have been true to me?"

There was a shocked silence. Not a tail twitched, not a paw stirred. The light went from Sita's eyes like moonlight stealing from a pond. She could not speak. They stood staring at one another, then Rama turned and walked away. Sita dropped her head, so none could see her face as tears began to roll down her cheeks. The creatures began to stir, but still no one spoke or moved from their place.

At last, Sita said, "Lakshmana, would you collect a great pile of wood, please?"

Lakshmana bowed to Sita and moved away, calling two of the strongest bear-warriors to help him. When a great pile of wood had been laid before Sita, she said to Lakshmana, "Noble brother, will you light the wood for me."

Lakshmana frowned. He looked around for a flaming torch. Not a flicker of fire could be seen. The animals all began to look about, but nobody seemed able to find a camp torch.

Hanuman bounded away while everyone else was searching. He found Rama alone in his tent.

"Rama, what are you thinking? Sita loves you best in all the world. She has asked Lakshmana to build a fire and light it. I fear what she will do next."

"She has been untrue to me", said Rama. "If she was not untrue, why did she not say so when I spoke to her?"

"Rama," said Hanuman, "I love you as my dearest brother, so I am telling you, you are a fool. Come now I beg you."

So Rama went with Hanuman back to the battlefield. But Sita had become impatient with the search for a torch and said, "Lakshmana, why do you hunt about, like this? Chant the sacred fire mantra so the fire god will light the wood for me."

Lakshmana could not deny Sita her wish. He called the fire god Agni to light the fire. As Hanuman and Rama returned to the battle-field, the fire blazed. Sita turned to her husband and said, "I love you with all my soul. Never have I been untrue to you. I have lived for your love." Then Sita walked into the blaze.

Rama and the grief-stricken animals looked on. The flames swirled around her but Sita did not burn. The great black curls and molten gold cloak of the fire god Agni appeared in the flames. Sparks flew from his eyes.

"Shame on you, Rama", he roared. "Sita is without fault. She waited for you, spurning the advances of Ravana. She never doubted you or thought of another. Such purity will not burn."

Agni walked from the fire with Sita, his blazing red and gold figure almost too bright to behold. Rama bowed his head before the fire god and his wife. He knew now it was himself, not Sita, who had failed in his love. Seeing the love return to his eyes, Sita went to her husband. Now truly they were together and would always trust one another. The bears and monkeys rejoiced and, this time, even the gods threw flowers from heaven.

Note:
Further information on the Ramayana can be found in the *Junior Teacher's Handbook*, page 114 and in the *Infant Teacher's Handbook*, pages 82 & 83.

Hanuman, the Child of the Wind   1/98 MSm

L ong, long, ago in India, lived the Lord of all the Winds. He had a son, whose name was Hanuman. If you or I looked at Hanuman, we might think he was just a little monkey, because that is what he looked like. But he was really a prince, a god, the son of the wind.

Hanuman grew up in the forest. He played with the deer and the elephants on the ground, and he played with the monkeys and the squirrels in the tree-tops. Because he was the son of the wind he even learnt to fly, so that he could play with the birds and the butterflies in the air.

But one morning, as he sat at the top of a tall tree, he saw someone he had never played with before. It was the sun, shining like a golden ball as it rose over the trees and sailed through the sky.

"It's lovely! I want it! I want to play with it!" cried Hanuman, and stretched out his arms. He jumped from his tree, and flew towards the sun, shouting, "Play with me! Play with me!"

But the sun did not hear what he was saying. The sun only saw Hanuman running towards her, which made her afraid. So the sun ran away from Hanuman, and ran, and ran, all over the sky, calling, "Save me! Save me!"

The great god Indra of a thousand eyes was passing by and he saw the sun running all over the sky.

"Who has frightened the sun?" he roared. He threw his spear at Hanuman, and Hanuman fell down, down, down to the earth below. The birds and the butterflies, the monkeys and the squirrels, the deer and the elephant all cried as they saw him fall.

But saddest of all was his father, the Lord of the Winds. He rushed down to the place where Hanuman had fallen. And as he passed, the waters were lashed into great waves, the trees bent and broke, and the animals hid in their caves. The Lord of the Winds gathered up his son in his arms and flew far, far away to the end of the earth.

When the Lord of the Winds had gone, peace came back to the earth. The waters became smooth again, the trees stood upright and grew new leaves, and the animals crept out of their caves and began to play again.

But something was wrong. With no wind, nothing could breathe. There was no air on the earth. The trees died, the birds and butterflies died. The squirrels and monkeys died, the deer and the elephants died. All was quiet. Nothing moved.

Once again Indra of a thousand eyes, king of the gods, passed by. He knew that he had made a terrible mistake. What could he do?

He travelled to the east and looked for the Lord of the Winds there, but he did not find him.

He travelled to the west and looked for the Lord of the Winds there, but he did not find him.

He travelled to the south and the north and looked for the Lord of the Winds there, but he did not find him.

He travelled up into the sky and looked for the Lord of the Winds there, but he did not find him.

He travelled down in to the earth and looked for the Lord of the Winds there. And there at last he found him, sitting in a dark, dark cave underneath the earth, crying over the body of his son.

"Forgive me!" cried Indra. "And do not be sad. Hanuman is not dead. He will grow up to be brave and powerful. Return to the world and his life will return."

The Lord of the Winds took his son's body in his arms and flew upwards to the earth. Gentle breezes followed him. Gradually the trees and flowers, the animals, the birds, the insects came to life again. Men, women, boys and girls yawned and stretched and looked around with delight. They felt they had awakened from a very, very deep sleep. Hanuman too returned to life, and began to play with his friends again as his father breathed gentle breezes over him.

And Hanuman grew up to be brave and strong and always helped people when they needed him.

All over India children are told the story of Hanuman. They sing songs about his great deeds, and promise to try to be like him and to help people.

Ganesha

Ganesha is a popular Hindu god, and there are many different stories told about his birth. This is one of them.

Lord Shiva whose dance creates and destroys the world is married to Parvati. Long ago, Parvati wanted a child but Shiva said that all creation was their child so they had no need for another.

When Parvati continued to plead, Shiva tugged playfully at her cloak and folded it into the shape of a baby boy. "Here's a son for you to kiss and cuddle as much as you wish", he said.

"Stop teasing me", said Parvati, pressing the cloth baby against her heart as if to fill it with love. As she did so the baby wriggled and cried "Mama". Looking down Parvati saw she was now holding a live baby. She kissed and hugged the baby in delight then held him up for Shiva saying, "Take your son, husband". But Shiva was annoyed that they now had a real baby and opened his third eye and looked at his son. Instantly the boy's head fell off.

Overcome with grief, Parvati desperately tried to put the head back on. Even Shiva, sorry at his rash deed, could not repair the head that had met the dreadful gaze of his third eye.

So Shiva sent his messenger Nandin to find another head for his son. He told Nandin the head must be facing north, as that was the direction the boy was facing when his head came off.

Nandin travelled about the universe until he came upon the elephant of Indra the sky god, resting with its head facing north. Nandin raised his sword to cut off the elephant's head but Indra saw and gave a shout of rage. When Nandin again made to cut off the elephant's head all the gods attacked him with a rain of arrows. But Nandin could not be stopped. He cut off the elephant's head, breaking one tusk in his hurry, and took it back to Shiva.

As soon as Shiva placed the elephant's head on his son's body the boy came to back to life.

When angry Indra and the other gods arrived, they could not help being glad at the sight of Shiva's beautiful son. Brahma, the father of all the gods, declared that the boy should be called Ganesha which means ruler-of-all-the-hosts. Only Shiva would be a more powerful ruler of the gods.

Shiva saw how sad Indra was at the death of his elephant and told him, "Throw your elephant's body into the ocean". When Indra obeyed, his elephant rose out of the waves with a new head.

Tales from Islam

Ibrahim and the Idols June '06

Muslims and Jews both have great respect for the Prophet Ibrahim (Jews call him Abraham). However they both tell slightly different stories about him. The following stories are from Islam.

When the Prophet Ibrahim was a boy, his father used to make idols – stone figures which people worshipped. Ibrahim soon realised that something was wrong with this. He couldn't understand why people worshipped carved lumps of stone which just sat there and couldn't do anything. But when he asked people why they worshipped the idols they just got annoyed with him. So, in the end, he decided to show the people how useless the idols were.

One day, while everyone was out celebrating a festival, Ibrahim went into the temple where the idols were kept. He started speaking to them and making fun of them, but of course they didn't say anything. Then he took an axe and started smashing them. He shattered all of them into little pieces – or rather, all except the biggest one. He had a special reason for not breaking that one. Instead, he hung the axe round its neck.

When everyone got back from the festival, people were horrified to see the idols all smashed up. "Who could have done this?" they asked. They thought about Ibrahim – he'd been saying some strange things about idols, and so they hunted for him and started to question him.

"Who broke the idols?" they asked Ibrahim.

"Don't ask me", said Ibrahim. "Ask that big idol there – the one with the axe round its neck!"

"Don't be so silly, Ibrahim, you know that idols can't speak."

"Who is being silly? You worship them – these idols which can't speak or move or do anything."

Now the people became really angry. They were so angry that they decided to burn Ibrahim; they built a huge fire and threw him into it. But a miracle happened! Ibrahim was not burnt, because Allah was protecting him. Not only was everyone astonished, but Ibrahim had also made the people think very hard about worshipping idols.

Hagar and Ishmael June 06

The Prophet Ibrahim lived in the desert with his wife, Sarah, and many servants. Once, he had lived in a big city teeming with people, but he had spurned their worship of idols and now sought to follow the one God. His life was a nomadic one, staying awhile in one place until his flocks had eaten all the green that had pushed its way upward through the stony surface. Then he and his household would pack their huge tents on to camels and move on to find another grazing ground. He was a wealthy man though, with a lot of livestock.

Although he was a wealthy man, Ibrahim lacked what makes a man truly wealthy – for he had no children, and to be blessed with children is the greatest wealth. For years he and his wife Sarah had longed for a child, but Sarah remained barren. Then one day Sarah came to Ibrahim and said, "If I cannot be a mother you can still be a father. Take my slave Hagar and make her your second wife. Perhaps she will bear you a child."

So Ibrahim took Hagar to be his second wife and a short time later she became pregnant. Now Hagar became boastful because she was carrying the child of Ibrahim, and she began to taunt her former mistress.

"You may have been a princess, and I only a slave. You may have been Ibrahim's first wife and I only his second, but I will be the mother of his child." And she would pat proudly her growing belly.

At first Sarah shrank in humiliation from these taunts, but as they grew stronger her humiliation changed to anger. She bitterly complained to Ibrahim, "I am your first wife and look what she is doing to me. I should not be treated in this way."

And Ibrahim told her she could deal with Hagar as she liked. So Sarah took her revenge on Hagar, using all her authority in the household to make Hagar's life a misery. Now it was Hagar's turn to weep with self pity. Soon her life became so unbearable that she decided to run away into the desert.

There an angel, a messenger from God found her. "Where have you come from? Why are you running away?" he asked her.

"I was the slave of Sarah, but now I am running from her. She is tormenting me because I am pregnant with her husband's child and she has none", replied Hagar.

"Return to Sarah," the angel told her, "and obey her – for she is the senior wife. But be comforted, for you will give birth to a son and his name will be Ishmael."

Hagar returned and gave birth to a boy whom she named Ishmael.

Fourteen years passed and Sarah too gave birth to a son – much to everyone's surprise, because they thought she was too old to have a child. Sarah called her son Isaac, and loved him with all her heart. But she was also worried for him. Ibrahim loved Hagar's son Ishmael – would he love Isaac as much?

"What if Ishmael should inherit Ibrahim's wealth?" she thought. "Then what will happen to Isaac? Ishmael may be his first son, but Isaac is the son of his first wife."

So she pleaded with Ibrahim. "Send away that woman and her son!" Morning and night she repeated her plea, but, although Ibrahim hated to see his wife so upset, he loved his son Ishmael and did not want to send him away. What was he to do ?

Then God spoke to him. "I will make your son Ishmael the father of a great people, and I will make your son Isaac the father of a great people."

So now Ibrahim could make his decision. He trusted God's promise – if Ishmael was to be the father of a great people then God would care for him. Ibrahim gave in to Sarah's demands and he sent out Ishmael and his weeping mother into the desert.

Once in the desert however it was not long before Hagar and her son were in trouble. The bread and water they had taken with them for their journey had not lasted very long. They were tired and hungry, and their throats were dry and parched as the hot sun beat relentlessly down on them.

"Mother, I am so tired. I can't go on!" said Ishmael.

"Lie here by this bush", said his mother.

Hagar gazed lovingly at her sleeping son. She was certain that they would both perish, and she couldn't bear to see him die. So she left him in the shade of the bush, and walked out into the desert, until she too collapsed with heat and exhaustion. As she lay there however a voice spoke to her, "Don't be afraid, Hagar, God will protect you and your son." She opened her eyes. There miraculously before her was a spring of cool clear water. At once she filled the bottle and hastened back to Ishmael.

Hagar and Ishmael lived in the wilderness as the boy grew into a man. God gave them his protection, and Ishmael's children and his children's children became a great nation as God had promised.

Note:
This story can be told in conjunction with work on 'Places of pilgrimage' in the *Junior Teacher's Handbook*, page 74.

Ibrahim and Ishmael

I brahim loved his son Ishmael dearly. He also loved Allah. Then one day it seemed that he would have to choose between the two. Allah had sent him a dream in which he was told that he was to sacrifice his son Ishmael. What was Ibrahim to do? If he killed Ishmael, then he would have lost the son he loved so much. If he didn't, he would have disobeyed Allah, whom he also loved.

Ibrahim decided that Allah must have a reason for asking him to sacrifice his son, although he couldn't understand it. He told Ishmael about his dream, and asked him what he should do. Ishmael said, "Do what you have been told, father. I am willing." So, with a heavy heart, Ibrahim prepared his son for sacrifice.

But just as the knife was about to fall, Allah spoke to Ibrahim, and said: "You have done what was needed". Ibrahim had passed the test. He had shown that he was willing to do anything for Allah – even lose the son he loved.

God sent a lamb for Ibrahim to sacrifice in Ishmael's place, and blessed Ibrahim and all his descendants.

Note:
Jews tell the story with Isaac as the intended sacrifice (see the story of 'Abraham and Isaac', page 128).

Muhammad

The year was 610 CE. The place was Mount Hira near Makkah in Saudi Arabia. There, in a cave on the mountain side, a man sat thinking. His name was Muhammad. He was well known in Makkah as a good and honest trader. He had a wife and children who loved him. But he often felt upset and puzzled by what he saw in the world around him. Many people were dishonest or unkind, and very few people took care of those who were hungry, poor or ill. There were people of many religions in Makkah, who worshipped many different gods. But it seemed to Muhammad that they did not think about what they were doing. Their beliefs did not help make them better or kinder people.

But what was the right religion and who was the true god? Muhammad could not tell, and he often spent several days and nights in this cave. There it was quiet and he could think and pray by himself.

Suddenly, Muhammad realised that he was not alone in the cave. An angel stood in front of him and said "Read!"

"I am not a reader", replied Muhammad, puzzled.

"Read!" said the angel again, and again Muhammad answered that he was not a reader.

Then the angel told him these words: "Read in the name of your Lord who created, created man from a clot of blood. Read, for your Lord is most generous. He who taught by the pen, taught man what he did not know."

Muhammad knew in his heart that this was a message from Allah, the true God that he had been searching for. He knew he would never forget the words spoken by the angel. But he was afraid. How could he be the one to have messages from Allah? How could he tell other people about this? Trembling with fear, he ran home to his wife Khadijah and told her all that had happened.

"What is to become of me?" he said.

"Don't worry," Khadijah comforted him, "I am sure Allah has chosen you to be his prophet. He will not let you down. And you have never done any harm to anyone. You are kind to others and you help the poor. If anyone is good enough to be God's messenger, you are that man."

A few months later Muhammad saw the angel again and he realized it was time to start telling people about Allah the one true God, and that they should stop worshipping other gods and should live as Allah wanted them to. Some people believed him and they became known as Muslims, from the Arabic word for 'obedience'. Many others were very angry.

"Who does he think he is?" they muttered. "What is wrong with our gods? Why should we give them up for this new religion?"

So one day Muhammad climbed a hill and spoke to the people of Mecca. He said, "If I told you there was an army on the other side of this hill which was going to attack you, would you believe me?"

The people said, "Yes, we have never known you to lie."

Then Muhammad told them, "Well, now I am warning you about something much more serious. You will be punished in this life and the next unless you believe that there is only one God."

Some of the people were offended by what Muhammad was saying and tried to stop him by offering him money. Others laughed at him and got children in the streets to throw rubbish at him. Some even plotted to kill him. But day after day Muhammad saw and heard the messages from God. He remembered every word, and he knew he could not be silent.

For over ten years Muhammad struggled to teach the words of Allah to the people of Makkah. Then, in 622 CE, he and the other Muslims moved to the city of Madinah, where the people welcomed them.

There Muhammad set up the first Muslim community. There the Muslims lived as sisters and brothers. They prayed to Allah, cared for each other as equals and lived as Allah wanted. But they always longed to return to the holy city of Makkah.

The people of Makkah still hated Muhammad and the Muslims. They sent armies to attack them in Madinah, and two great battles were fought. Many people died, but the Muslims were glad to give up their lives fighting for what they believed was right.

After many years of bitter struggle, the Muslim army finally took Makkah by surprise and joyfully entered the city. The people of Makkah were terrified. Would the Muslims punish them for so many years of fighting? But Muhammad gave orders that no one should be hurt, so long as they stopped fighting against the Muslims. And when they saw how fair and wise Muhammad was, many people in Makkah felt that they had been wrong to hate him and his religion, and became Muslims themselves.

Soon after this, Muhammad died. Muslims travelled to many parts of the world, and today millions of people pray to Allah as the one true God. They read the words that Muhammad heard from Allah, for the early Muslims wrote them down and collected them into a holy book called the Qur'an. Muslims today also read about Muhammad's life, because his companions remembered the kind things he had done, the wise things he had said and even the way he did ordinary everyday things. They told other people and eventually these things were written down in books. These traditions are called the Hadith. In this way, Muslims can follow Muhammad's example in obeying Allah in everything they do.

Muslims are thankful to Allah for sending them the Prophet Muhammad. They believe that, although other prophets had spoken Allah's words before, Muhammad said everything that Allah wanted to tell people. He was Allah's last and greatest prophet.

Whenever Muslims speak or write the name of Muhammad,

they add the words "Peace be upon him" to give thanks to Allah for his life and his message.

Note:
This story can be told in conjunction with work on 'Where do rules come from?' in the *Junior Teacher's Handbook*, page 60. Further information about Muhammad can be found in the *Infant Teacher's Handbook*, page 88 and in the *Junior Teacher's Handbook*, page 119.

The Woman at the Gate of Makkah

There are many traditions about the life of Muhammad. Here is one of them.

A man sat at the gate of the city of Makkah, gazing out at the road which led to the next town. He was good-looking, and you could see kindness in his face. But just now the lines of tiredness and sadness were more clearly to be seen. With a sigh he stood up and turned to go back into the city. But coming the other way he saw an old woman, laden down with bags and bundles, hurrying along the road out of the city. She was clearly upset, and her bags kept slipping ·from her grip.

"Good day!" said the man. "That's a heavy burden you bear. Let me take some of your bags. Here, give me that heavy one, and the one that's hung round your neck. There, that's better. I'll carry these wherever you're going."

"Oh, thank you sir!" gasped the old woman. "But I'm going to the next city. You won't want to go so far to help me."

"It's no trouble at all, you're welcome", said the man. "But tell me, why are you leaving Makkah in such a hurry?"

"Oh, I can't stay a moment longer! Haven't you heard? There's this man Muhammad going about trying to make people follow a new religion! He's upsetting everyone, and telling them not to worship idols the way our fathers did, and their fathers before them. And they say he has powers to bewitch people! People fall under his spell, and do what he says, and pray to Allah, and they won't stop, even when their parents or their wives plead with them. Why, there are even slaves who are following Muhammad, and they've been tortured and killed, but they still won't give up!"

The man's face grew even sadder. "Yes," he said, "there are terrible things happening in Makkah."

"So I'm leaving quick, before I fall under the spell of this Muhammad! I don't want to follow a man like that! Oh, if only there were more kind and considerate people like you in Makkah, then we wouldn't be in this state! I'd take the advice of someone like you, no problem! You're so kind. Tell me, what is your name?"

The man stopped, and put down the bag he was carrying.

"My name", he said, "is Muhammad, and I pray to Allah, the one true God."

"In that case, " said the woman, "I have only one thing to say to you! Would you be so kind as to pick up my bag, and help me back to Makkah?"

Note:
This story can be told in conjunction with work on 'How do we learn?', in the *Junior Teacher's Handbook*, page 42.

How 'Umar became a Muslim

When Muhammad first started preaching in Makkah, telling people about Allah, and saying that they should pray to Allah as the one true God, many people were against him, and thought that his message was wrong. One of these people was a young man called 'Umar. It seems he was a man of action, big, strong and tough. When he heard about Muhammad's teaching, he decided to do something about it. Immediately he set off towards Muhammad's house, his face hard and determined.

On the way he met a friend of his.

"Where are you going, 'Umar, with that fierce look on your face?" asked his friend."

I'm off to Muhammad's house to kill him!" said 'Umar. "He is teaching dangerous nonsense in this city, and he has to be stopped!"

"I don't know about Muhammad," said 'Umar's friend. "Maybe it's not up to you to deal with him. Why don't you start closer to home? What about your own sister, Fatimah?"

"What do you mean?" gasped 'Umar, horrified.

"Didn't you know?" replied his friend. "People are saying she's become a Muslim – she and her husband, Sa'id. They try to keep it a secret, because Muslims are in danger now. But I think you ought to know."

"What!" roared 'Umar. "My own family, my own sister! I'll deal with them!" And he turned and headed for Fatimah's house.

As he came near, he heard a voice from inside the house. The voice seemed to be reciting poetry, but 'Umar was too angry to listen. Without knocking or stopping at the door, he charged into his sister's house.

"What's this nonsense I hear?" he roared, rushing from room to room, searching for his sister. There seemed to be something going on at the back of the house, but before he could find out what it was, Fatimah and Sa'id appeared, looking scared and out of breath.

"Who was that I heard just now? What was he reading? That wasn't Sa'id's voice! What's going on?"

"My dear brother," faltered Fatimah, "it's good to see you. Sit down and let me bring you some coffee and dates."

"Never mind that!" shouted 'Umar. "Tell me what you were listening to!"

"No," said Fatimah and Sa'id, as calmly as they could, "we will not tell you, for you would not respect it."

"Tell me," roared 'Umar, "or I'll alter your husband's face for him!" And he grabbed Sa'id and began to hit him.

"No! Leave him! What harm has he done you?" cried Fatimah, and rushed forward to throw herself between 'Umar and Sa'id. As she did so, one of 'Umar's punches landed on her face, and she staggered back, bleeding. 'Umar let go of Sa'id and leaned against the wall, gasping.

"Fatimah! I'm sorry! I didn't mean to hurt you! But what is going on? What was that poetry I heard? Why won't you tell me?"

Fatimah and Sa'id looked at each other, and Sa'id took a deep breath. "We will tell you", he said. "We will show it to you, but you must treat it with respect. Wash your hands now, if you want to see what we were reading. For you must have guessed – we are indeed Muslims, and we were reading Allah's message that He gave to Muhammad."

So 'Umar washed his hands, and they brought out a sheet of paper and began to read. The words were in Arabic, in the most beautiful poetry. It is impossible to give you an idea of how beautiful those words seemed to 'Umar, or how beautiful they are to Muslims today, but the meaning was something like this:

"Allah's message is not sent to distress you, but only as a warning. It is to tell you about Him who created the earth and the heavens on high. Allah, the most gracious, is firmly established on His throne. Everything that is in the heavens and on earth belong to Him; everything between the heavens and the earth; everything that is beneath the soil. Whether you speak aloud or not, Allah knows what is hidden and what is secret. Allah! There is no God but He! To Him belong the most beautiful names!" (adapted from S. 20, verses 1-8)

As he listened, something happened to 'Umar. The words were so beautiful, and struck him as being so true, that he decided then and there that he had been wrong about Muhammad and his message. "Lead me to him," said 'Umar, "so that I can learn more from him and become a Muslim."

"There is no need for you to go anywhere", said Fatimah and Sa'id. "There is someone here who can teach you: Muhammad's friend Khabbab is hiding at the back of our house. It was his voice you heard when you came, but we hid him when we saw how angry you were. Come now and meet him, and he will explain Allah's message to you."

From that time on 'Umar became one of the most faithful Muslims, and he used his bravery and strength in the struggle for Islam.

And many years later, after Muhammad had died, he became one of the leaders of the Muslim community.

Note:
This story can be told in conjunction with work on 'Eid Ul-Fitr' in the *Infant Teacher's Handbook*, page 66.

Muhammad Washing

O ne day, when the Prophet Muhammad was on a journey, he and his companions stopped to rest by a stream. The water flowed cool and clear and plentiful.

The day was hot, and their feet and hands and faces were very dusty. Gratefully they went down to the stream to wash. The Prophet's companions dipped their feet and hands into the water and let it flow over them. They splashed their faces with the lovely cool water. But then they stopped in amazement as they saw what their Prophet, Muhammad, was doing. From his pack he took a small bowl and dipped it in the stream. Then he scooped up a small amount of water in his hands and washed his face, then his hands. Then he washed his feet, still using the same small bowlful of water.

"Why do you do that, O Prophet?" they asked. "There is plenty of water in the stream, and yet you act as though that bowlful was all you could have for washing!"

"Allah gives us good gifts," replied the Prophet, "and he gives enough for all. But even when there is plenty, we should never waste even the tiniest part of what he has given us."

―❖▢❖―

The Thirsty Camel

A fter the Muslims had established themselves at Madinah, they planted gardens and trees. One day Muhammad was walking through Madinah and came to a particularly pleasant garden. One man was sitting in the shade of a tree, and others were sitting in cool parts of the garden. In one corner was a camel tied to a post and howling. Muhammad went over to it and saw that it was in great distress. Not only was it tied up in the full heat of the sun, it was thin and exhausted and in poor condition.

Muhammad stroked and soothed the camel for a while, until it became calmer. Then he turned to the people in the garden.

"Whose camel is this?" he asked.

"It's mine", said the man in the shade of the tree.

"Aren't you ashamed of yourself?" said the prophet. "Allah has entrusted this creature to you, for it to help you by working for you, but also for you to care for it. This is one of God's living creatures, and you are responsible for its wellbeing. How dare you sit at your ease in the shade, when the creature entrusted to your care is suffering!"

Note:
This story can be told in conjunction with the work on the 'Natural world' in the *Junior Assembly Book*, page 15.

Tales from Judaism

The Promise to Abraham

Abram lived many centuries ago in the city of Ur of Chaldees with his wife Sarai. Ur was a big city for those times, traders selling their wares bustled about its streets; herdsmen brought in their stock to the marketplaces; the place was a hive of activity. The people of Ur worshipped many gods. The statues of them stood in shrines in the marketplaces, and were bought for the home. But Abram mocked the worship of gods of stone and turned to worship the one true god, creator of all.

Now the Lord God said to Abram, "Leave your country, your family and your father's house and travel to the land I will show you, and I will bless you and make your name famous."

And Abram obeyed God. He left his country, his family and his father's house and began the life of a nomad in the desert. He took with him his wife Sarai, his nephew Lot and many slaves and possessions. Together they crossed the land of the Caananites. Wherever they found water and good grass they pitched their tents, grazed their flocks and stayed for a while. And wherever they pitched their tents Abram built an altar to the Lord God.

Now, Abram and his wife Sarai had no children because Sarai

was barren. Sarai longed for a child, so one day she came to Abram and said, "The Lord God has prevented me having children. Why don't you father a child by my Egyptian slave girl, Hagar?" Abram agreed with this idea for he too longed for a son, and Hagar gave birth to a boy whom they named Ishmael.

When Abram was ninety-nine years old, the Lord God appeared to him and he said: "I will make a promise to you, a covenant between myself and your family. Your name will no longer be Abram but Abraham which means father of a multitude. Your descendants will be as many as the stars in the sky and the grains of sand on the beach. Your wife Sarai shall have a new name. She shall be called Sarah, the mother of kings. I will bless her and she shall give birth to a son. You shall call his name Isaac. You and your sons must bear the mark of the covenant on your bodies by being circumcised."

But Abram was puzzled by this, for his wife Sarai was very old and past the age of child bearing – and what of his son Ishmael? What would happen to him?

Abraham cried out to the Lord God for the sake of Ishmael and the Lord God replied, "Ishmael will also be a father of a great nation, but my covenant will be with the child of Sarah and his children and his children's children."

Abraham obeyed God and he and his son Ishmael, and all the males of the household were circumcised.

A short time later, Abraham was sitting in the entrance to the tent during the hottest part of the day. He looked up to see three strangers standing before him. He knew at once that they were messengers from the Lord God and he ran forward to welcome them. He bowed to them and begged them to stay awhile. "Refresh yourselves before you go any further. I will fetch you some water and you can have some bread."

He rushed back to Sarah in the tent, calling to her to make some bread, and he ordered that the finest calf should be prepared as a meal for his honoured guests.

As they sat together, these words of the Lord God were said to Abraham, "Next year I will visit you without fail and your wife Sarah will have a son."

Sarah was standing behind the tent and she laughed to herself "I am a very old woman. It's been a long time since I could have a child. Me – have a son? Impossible!"

But the Lord God kept his promise and Sarah did conceive and bear a son in her old age. She called his name Isaac as the Lord God had commanded, and he was the joy and delight of his mother's life and the pride of his father Abraham.

And Isaac became the father of Esau and Jacob, and Jacob had twelve sons. The Lord God renewed his covenant with Isaac and Jacob and with their descendants after them. Still today the Jewish people speak of their fathers of long ago – Abraham, Isaac and Jacob. Their wives Sarah, Rebekah and Rachel are called 'mothers of the people'.

Note:
Further information on Abraham's Covenant with God can be found on page 91 of the *Infant Teacher's Handbook* and page 125 of the *Junior Teacher's Handbook*.

Abraham and Isaac

Abraham and his wife Sarah were very old, and they had no children. It was many years since they had even hoped for a child. Then, God made a promise to Abraham – a strange, unbelievable promise – that they would have a son. Abraham laughed when he heard God's promise, and so did Sarah, yet they did indeed have a son, whom they called Isaac, which means laughter.

Isaac was very precious to Abraham and Sarah, and they took great care of him. Then one day, Abraham was asked to do the hardest thing he had ever done in his life: to give up his son. God spoke to Abraham and said, "Take your son Isaac whom you love so much, and go up into a mountain. Offer him as a sacrifice on the altar, as if he were one of the animals which are sacrificed to me."

Abraham's heart was heavy as he got up early the next morning. He saddled his donkey, chopped up firewood for the altar, and took Isaac to the mountains with two servants. They travelled for three weary days. At last, they came near to the mountain which God had chosen. Abraham stopped. He said to the servants,

"Wait here with the donkey while Isaac and I go to worship." He gave the wood to Isaac to carry, while he carried a knife and a burning torch for the fire, and they walked up the mountain together.

As they walked, Isaac turned to his father and said, "Father, I don't understand. We have wood and fire, but where is the lamb we are going to sacrifice?"

Abraham replied, "God will provide a lamb for the sacrifice, my son."

They reached the top of the mountain, and there Abraham built an altar. He piled the wood on to it. Then, with tears in his eyes, he tied up his beloved son and placed him on the firewood. He took the knife in his hand and prepared to plunge it into Isaac.

Suddenly, a voice spoke to him. "Do not harm the boy. Now you have shown how much you love me. You were prepared to give me everything, even your son whom you love so much."

Abraham looked round, and there, caught by its horns in a bush, was a ram. God had indeed provided a sacrifice and, because of his faith, he blessed Abraham and Isaac, and all their descendants.

Note:
Muslims tell the story with Ishmael as the intended sacrifice (see the story of 'Ibrahim and Ishmael' page 116).

Jacob and Esau

Jacob and Esau were brothers. They were twins, and even before they were born, it seemed that they were fighting. Their mother, Rebekah, could feel them kicking and struggling inside her. Esau was born first, so he was the eldest. But Jacob was born holding onto Esau's heel. As they grew up, like many children, they went on quarrelling.

"I am the eldest", said Esau. "You must do what I say."

"But I got hold of your heel", said Jacob. "That shows that I am the boss!"

"But I am the eldest", said Esau. "That means I will have all our father's land when he dies, and all his sheep and all his goats and all his cows. And I will have the special blessing from God, the blessing he gave to our grandfather Abraham, the blessing he gave to our father Isaac. That will be mine when he dies, because I am the eldest."

To make matters worse, their mother and father took sides. Esau was good at running and fighting and throwing the spear, and his father, Isaac, thought he was the best son. Jacob was clever and quick-thinking. He grew vegetables for his mother in his garden, so she thought he was the best son.

When they grew up, they still lived with their mother and father, but they did not quarrel so much, because they did not see each other very much. Esau became a hunter, and spent many days, even weeks, out in the forest in search of the animals he hunted. Jacob became a farmer, and stayed at home looking after the fields and the sheep and cows.

One day, Esau had been away in the forest for many days. He was very tired and very hungry. He saw Jacob sitting with a pot full of good, thick soup, and he said, "Please give me some of your soup!"

But Jacob replied, "I will only give you some if you sell me your rights as the eldest son. I want to have the land, the sheep and the cows. And I want to have the blessing from God."

"All right", said Esau. "Just now I'm so hungry I don't care! You can have them."

"Is that a solemn promise?" said Jacob.

"Yes, yes, I swear you can have it all. Just give me some soup!"

So Esau ate the soup and went away happy. And Jacob stirred his soup and sat there, even more happy. Now he would count as the eldest son.

But Isaac did not know about any of this. As time went by, Isaac grew very old, and he could not see very well. He knew he would die soon, so he called Esau to him and said: "Go hunting for me one more time. Catch some tasty meat and bring me the kind of food I like. Then I will give you all my riches, and the blessing from God."

So Esau set off hunting. But his mother Rebekah was listening, and as soon as he had gone she called Jacob.

"Quick," she said, "bring me two of your young goats, and I will make some of the food that Isaac likes. Then you can pretend to be Esau, and take the food to him, and he will give you all his riches, and the blessing from God."

"But he'll know I'm not Esau", said Jacob. "Our voices are different, and we dress differently. And when he touches me he'll know, because Esau has hairy arms, and mine are smooth."

"That's easy," said Rebekah, "put some of the skin of the goat over your arm, so that it feels hairy. I'll give you some of Esau's clothes to put on, and you can imitate Esau's voice, can't you?"

So Jacob did as his mother said. He went in to his father and said: "Here is the food you asked me for, father. Eat it and give me your blessing."

"Who's that?" asked Isaac.

"It's me, Esau", said Jacob in his gruffest voice.

"How quickly you found the animal to kill!" said Isaac.

"God sent me his help", said Jacob, trying not to speak too much.

"Are you sure you're my son Esau?" said Isaac. "It doesn't sound like Esau. Come here and let me feel you."

So Jacob went up to his father and let him feel the goatskin over his arm. Isaac felt it, and he smelt the smell of Esau's clothes that Jacob was wearing, and a look of puzzlement came over his face. "You feel and smell like Esau, but the voice is the voice of Jacob. Maybe my hearing's going too. It must be you, Esau. I will eat your food."

When Isaac had finished eating, he gave Jacob all his riches, and the blessing from God. So Jacob went out a happy man. But as soon as he had gone, Esau came back with the animals he had hunted. He cooked the meat, and took it to his father Isaac.

"Here you are, father. Eat this and then give me your riches, and the blessing from God."

"Who are you?" said Isaac, for he could not see well.

"I am Esau, your son. You told me to bring you food", said Esau.

"Then who was that who has just gone? Who was that I gave my riches to, and the blessing from God?"

"Jacob! It must have been Jacob! Oh, how I hate him! He has taken everything! Can't you get it back, and give it to me?"

"I can't do that, my son", said Isaac. "I have promised, and I cannot break my promise."

"Then can't you give me something else? It's not fair!" cried Esau.

"I gave him everything. There is nothing left for you", said Isaac.

From that time on, Esau hated his brother Jacob, and made plans to kill him. But Rebekah heard him making plans. She said to Jacob, "Quick, get away from here to a safe place. Your brother won't be angry for ever. When he calms down again, I will let you know, and you can come back."

So Jacob took his sheep and goats, and travelled far away. But it was many, many years before he met his brother Esau again. And even then, he was so frightened of him that he sent hundreds of presents, to try and put him in a good mood, before he dared meet him. And then, to his astonishment, Esau ran forward and hugged him. He did not even mention what had gone on between them all those years earlier. And Jacob felt quite humble in front of his brother, who had forgiven him.

The Story of Joseph

1. Jealousy *May 07*

Jacob had 12 sons, but Joseph was his favourite. Joseph had been born when Jacob was already getting quite old, and that may have been why he loved Joseph more than all the others. He treated Joseph better, didn't ask him to work as hard as the others, and gave him better clothes. He gave Joseph a rich robe, decorated with many colours – a robe that might have been worn by the head of the family, not the second to youngest son! And as you might expect, Joseph's brothers hated him for it.

Joseph himself didn't help matters much. He told his father when his brothers were not looking after the sheep properly. He also told his brothers about the dreams he had.

"Listen," he said one morning, "I dreamed last night that we were all binding sheaves of corn, and suddenly the sheaf that I was binding stood upright, and all the sheaves that you were binding gathered round my sheaf and bowed down to it!"

"What are you saying?" said his brothers. "Are you intending to rule over us? Just don't you try it, young 'un!"

But it made no difference to Joseph. Next time he had a dream, he not only told his brothers about it, he told his father.

"This time", he said, "I dreamed that the sun and the moon and even the stars all bowed down to me!"

And to his brothers' fury, their father took it seriously!

"Does it mean that one day your mother and I, and all your brothers, will bow down to you?" Jacob wondered. The brothers gnashed their teeth and glared at Joseph, but in front of their father they did not dare to say anything.

But it was not long before their chance came. All the older brothers were out looking after the sheep, and travelling wherever there was grass to feed them. Jacob sent Joseph to see how they were getting on, and bring back a report. As Joseph travelled towards his brothers, they saw him coming in the distance.

"Here comes that dreamer!" they said to each other. "Now's our chance! Why don't we kill him, and tell our father that some wild animal must have attacked him. Then we'll see what comes of his dreams!"

But the eldest brother Reuben didn't want to see Joseph killed.

"We shouldn't shed any blood", he said to his brothers. "Look, there's a deep well here. Throw him in and leave him. That way we won't have his blood on our hands." Reuben's plan was to go back secretly to rescue Joseph and take him back to his father.

So when Joseph arrived, his brothers seized him, stripped him of his magnificent robe, and threw him down the well, which had no water in it. They then sat down to eat their meal, and as they were eating, they saw a party of merchants travelling by. These merchants were on their way to Egypt with spices. Judah, one of the brothers, had an idea.

"Let's haul Joseph up and sell him as a slave to these merchants. He'll get carried off to Egypt, and he'll never escape from there. We can put some blood on his robe and take it back to our father, and say that the wild animals killed Joseph. That way, we'll have the money, and we won't be guilty of killing our own brother. But we'll still be rid of him for good!"

When the brothers returned to Jacob with the richly coloured coat, all covered in the blood of a goat they had killed, Jacob was overcome with grief. His family tried to comfort him, but he was in despair.

"Don't try to bring me any comfort!" he cried. "I will spend the rest of my life in mourning for Joseph, and in mourning I will go to my grave!"

2. *Joseph in Slavery* May 07

Meanwhile, the merchants took Joseph to Egypt, and sold him to a man named Potiphar, who was captain of the guard in the court of the Pharaoh, the ruler of Egypt. Joseph worked hard, and God was with him. Everything he did went well. It wasn't long before Potiphar noticed this and, little by little, Joseph was put in charge of more and more of Potiphar's household, until he was actually running everything, and Potiphar trusted him with all his business.

For a while everything went well, but then Potiphar's wife made trouble. She fell in love with Joseph, and kept pestering him and following him round. Joseph said to her: "I am your husband's slave, and he trusts me with everything. It would be wrong for you and me to have anything to do with each other. You must leave me alone!"

But Potiphar's wife would not leave him alone. In the end she made up a story to get Joseph into trouble with her husband. He believed everything his wife told him, and he was so angry that he had Joseph put in prison.

But even in prison, God was with Joseph. It seemed that whatever he did was right, and it wasn't long before the governor of the prison trusted Joseph just as much as Potiphar had done. Although he was a slave and a prisoner, he was put in charge of running the prison!

Some time later, two new prisoners arrived. They had been important people in Pharaoh's court: his baker and his personal cupbearer. But somehow they had offended Pharaoh, and he had put them both in prison. One morning Joseph saw them both with troubled faces.

"What is it?" he said. "What's bothering you both?"

They explained that they had each had a dream in the night, and did not understand what their dreams meant. The cupbearer had dreamed that he had squeezed some grapes over Pharaoh's cup, and Pharaoh had drunk the juice. The baker had dreamed that he was carrying loaves to Pharaoh, but the birds had kept picking at the loaves.

"God is the one who explains dreams", said Joseph. "This is what God says your dreams mean. The cupbearer will soon be restored to Pharaoh's favour, and will be free from prison. When that happens," he said, turning to the cupbearer, "don't forget me. I am in prison through no fault of my own, and you could put in a good word for me. But you," he said, turning to the baker, "I'm sorry to tell you that Pharaoh is going to have you killed."

In three day's time Joseph's words came true. The baker was put to death, but the cupbearer was taken out of prison and given his old job back. But he did not put in a good word for Joseph. He forgot all about him.

Two years passed, and then Pharaoh himself had two dreams that worried and puzzled him. He asked all the wise people at his court what they thought the dreams meant, but no one could explain them. At last Pharaoh's cupbearer came to him and said:

"I've got a guilty conscience, because I have done nothing about this for two years. But I remember a man called Joseph that I met in prison when you were angry with me. He was able to explain dreams, and everything he said came true. I promised to put in a good word for him, but I forgot about him until now. If you send for him, he may be able to tell you what your dream means."

So they sent for Joseph from prison, and when he had been smartened up a bit, they brought him to Pharaoh, who said, "I hear you can explain dreams."

"No", said Joseph, "I can't. Only God can do that, but if you tell me your dream, maybe God will explain it to me."

So Pharaoh told him: "I dreamed I was standing by the river Nile, and I saw seven fat, healthy cows come up from the river. They were followed by seven thin, diseased-looking cows. The thin cows ate up the fat cows – and after that I woke up. But when I fell asleep again, I dreamed I saw seven ears of corn on one stalk. They were good, fat, healthy ears of corn. But then seven more ears sprouted, and they were small, shrivelled and dried up. These seven shrivelled ears ate up the fat, healthy ears. Those were my dreams, and no one in my court can explain them to me."

"Your two dreams both mean the same thing", said Joseph. "God is showing you what is going to happen. There will be seven years in which the harvest will be plentiful, and everyone will have more than enough to eat. But these will be followed by seven years of drought and famine, and no one will remember the years of plenty, because they will be so hungry. What I suggest you do is this: Find someone you trust and put them in charge of storing food. In each of the good years they must collect corn from all over the land of Egypt and store it carefully. Then when the bad years come, there will be enough grain stored up to feed everyone."

"I'll do it!" said Pharaoh. "As for finding someone I can trust to be in charge of the collection, what better person could I find than you yourself, Joseph? God has explained my dreams to you, and showed you what is going to happen. The prison governor tells me that everything you do is done well, so I am going to put you in charge. I will give you my ring as a sign that you have my authority, and there will be no one in the whole kingdom greater than you, except myself."

3. Joseph in Charge   *May '07*

So Joseph once again wore fine clothes. He had a chariot to ride in, and wherever he went, people shouted out: "Make way! Make way!" because he was such an important person. For seven years he travelled round Egypt making sure that people did not eat all the grain that they grew, but stored one-fifth of it. The mountains of grain grew higher and higher, till there was so much that even Joseph stopped trying to keep account of it.

Eventually the good years were over, and the famine began. Then from all over Egypt, people came to Joseph, and he shared out the stored grain, and year after year, although the harvest was very bad, the people of Egypt had enough to eat.

It was not only in Egypt that the bad years came. People from many other lands came to Joseph asking to buy food. One day ten men arrived from the land of Canaan. They were ushered into

Joseph's presence, and he recognised them at once. But he hid his feelings, and they did not recognise him. He heard them speak to each other in the language of Canaan, the language of his boyhood, but he pretended he could not understand them, and he spoke only in the Egyptian language, using an interpreter to translate his words.

"Who are you, and what do you want?" he demanded sternly.

"My Lord," they replied, bowing low, "we have come to buy food. We are brothers from the land of Canaan. Once there were twelve of us. One brother, the youngest, has stayed behind with our father Jacob, and the other is dead."

His own brothers, who had sold him into slavery! How could they stand there and say to his face that their brother was dead! Maybe they really believed that he must have died all those years ago. Joseph decided to test them. Was the family still full of jealousy and hatred? He put on a stern look.

"You're not here to buy food! You're spies! You've come to see where Egypt is unprotected, so that your country can attack us!"

"No, no!" said the brothers. "We swear it! We have only come to buy food! Our father and youngest brother are waiting for us back in Canaan. Let us buy grain and go. Look, here is the money!"

Joseph pretended to consider. "I am still not convinced by your story", he said. "This is how I will test you. I am putting you all in prison for three days. Then I will choose one of you to stay here in prison while the rest of you go back to Canaan and fetch your youngest brother. If you return with him, all well and good, I will believe your story. If not, your brother here in prison will die!"

Three days later, Joseph had all ten of them brought before him again. He ran his eye sternly over all of them, as if choosing a victim. The ten brothers began to talk amongst themselves in their own language, thinking he could not understand them.

"That terrible thing we did, all those years ago", said one. "It's caught up with us now. We sold our brother to the Egyptians, and now we are prisoners in Egypt. We should never have done it!"

"He pleaded with us," said another, "but we wouldn't listen. Now we are being punished for it!"

"Didn't I tell you?" said Reuben. "I told you not to harm him, but you wouldn't listen! How can we say we are innocent men, when we know what we did to Joseph!"

Joseph could feel the tears pricking his eyes. Perhaps they were sorry after all! But he must not weaken yet. He turned away from them and struggled to stop the tears and keep a hard expression on his face. He turned back and pointed to his brother Simeon.

"That one will stay here", he said, still speaking through the interpreter. "You others, take the grain you have paid for, and go. Return with your youngest brother, or this one dies!"

And he swept from the room just in time to prevent them seeing him burst into tears. Then he gave orders to fill their bags with the grain that they had come to buy, but along with the grain, to put the money that each had paid. Then his servants loaded up the donkeys, gave the brothers food and water for the journey, and sent them on their way.

When the brothers stopped for the night, they discovered the silver in the sacks.

"What shall we do?" they said to each other. "How can we return to Egypt now? They will think we are thieves, as well as spies."

When they reached home and told their father Jacob what had happened, he bowed his head in despair.

"My son Joseph is dead," he mourned, "my son Simeon is lost to me, and will die in Egypt. I cannot let Benjamin go there, my youngest, my dearest after Joseph. I will die in sorrow for my sons."

4. Return to Egypt

But it was not long before the grain that they had bought in Egypt ran out, and still there was no sign of the end of the drought, and nothing to eat in Canaan.

"My sons," said Jacob, "you will have to go back to Egypt and buy more grain."

"How can we go?" they asked. "The official in charge told us that we were not to return without our youngest brother, or we would all be killed. He meant it, too. You should have seen his face! He's a hard man."

"Why ever did you tell him that you had a younger brother?" wailed Jacob in despair. "Couldn't you just have kept quiet about it?"

"But he asked so many questions – all about our family. Were there any other brothers? Was our father still alive? He wanted to know everything! And we just answered his questions. How were we to know what he was going to do?"

"But I cannot let Benjamin go with you. I know I will never see him again if he goes, and there will be no comfort left in my life. He must not leave me!"

"Father," Judah spoke quietly, "I will be responsible for him. I will bring him safely back to you, or I will bear the blame the rest of my life – the blame as if I had killed him with my own hands. I will bring him back, I swear it."

And so Jacob was gradually persuaded to part with his son, and the party set off back to Egypt. They took gifts of spices, nuts and honey, and they took the money that they had found in their sacks, as well as money to pay for the next lot of grain.

They were very nervous as they approached the city, but as soon as Joseph saw them, and saw that Benjamin was with them, he released Simeon from prison, and gave orders that they were to be treated well.

"Do not accept their money," he said, "but give them all the grain they can carry." Joseph met them, and talked with them, and especially to his brother Benjamin. He was so overcome with emotion as he spoke to Benjamin that he had to keep leaving the room to weep. How he longed to embrace them all and to be friends! But he had to put them to the last and hardest test.

Joseph told the servants to put the money for the grain in their sacks, as before.

"But also", he said, "take my own personal silver cup, and put it in the sack of the youngest. Then see them on their way back to Canaan."

As soon as they had gone he sent his servants after them. "Tell them that my cup is missing, and you are going to search all of their bags", said Joseph. And the servants did so.

The brothers were horrified. "Why would we steal a cup?" they demanded. "We are honest men, and you have treated us well. None of us has taken it! If you find the cup in any of our bags, then that man will die, and the rest of us will become your slaves. We have not taken it!"

When the cup was found in Benjamin's sack, they were in despair. Numb with grief, they reloaded their donkeys and returned to the city. They were taken to Joseph, and threw themselves at his feet.

"What have you done?" thundered Joseph.

"My Lord," faltered Judah, "we did not steal the cup. But how can we prove our innocence? Let the rest of us be your slaves for ever, but let my youngest brother Benjamin return to his father."

"No!" said Joseph. "Why should you all suffer for the fault of one? You have no choice in the matter. Your brother stays here, and the rest of you go back to your father."

"No, my Lord, I cannot do that", insisted Judah. He told Joseph about the promise he had made to his father Jacob. "It will kill him if Benjamin does not return", said Judah. "And I cannot go back and tell him that I left Benjamin here. Take me, make me your slave, kill me, do what you like to me, but let Benjamin return to his father!"

At this Joseph could contain himself no more. He turned to the Egyptian servants who were with him.

"Leave us!" he ordered in a harsh voice. As soon as they had gone, he burst into tears and told his brothers who he was. He hugged each one of them, and told them: "Do not be distressed at what you did all those years ago. God meant it to happen, so that now I can save your lives, and the life of my father Jacob, now that the famine has come. The hard times are not over yet. There will be five more years of famine still. Go back to our father, and persuade him to come and live in Egypt. You will all be welcome, you, your families, and everyone. Take as many carts and donkeys as you need, bring everyone, and let me see my father again!"

So they returned to Jacob and told him, "Joseph is alive! He is in charge of things in Egypt, and wants us all to go and live there!"

At first Jacob refused to believe them. He had been so anxious and sad that he could not take it in. But when the others described Joseph to him, and told him what they had talked about, he revived, and said at last, "I'm convinced! My son Joseph is still alive. I will go and see him before I die."

And that was how Jacob and all his sons, and his sons' children, left the land of Canaan and went to live in Egypt.

The Israelites Escape from Egypt

1. The birth of Moses

Long, long, ago there lived in the land of Egypt, the people of Israel. They had dwelt side by side with the Egyptians since the time of their ancestors Jacob and Joseph, who had been welcomed to Egypt by the Pharaoh. But time passed and the Pharaohs forgot their friendship with the people of Israel.

Then there came to the throne of Egypt a Pharaoh who was frightened of the Israelites.

"Look at them all", he said. "Soon they will overrun the country. They could destroy this land by helping our enemies."

So Pharaoh decided to make the people of Israel slaves and he set them to work building his new cities. Life became terrible for the Israelites. The slave drivers knew no mercy and the work was crushingly hard.

But still the Pharaoh feared the Israelites. So he commanded that all baby boy Israelites must be killed. In this way he hoped to stop the growing numbers of Israelites. Great was the sorrow and terror amongst the Israelites when news of Pharaoh's cruelty was heard. Many mothers tried to hide their babies. One mother managed to do so for three months, but then, with the baby growing bigger day by day, she became frightened. So she made a special basket, placed the baby in the basket and took the child down to the river. There she hid the basket in the bulrushes, and leaving the boy's sister to watch what happened, returned home.

Soon, the daughter of Pharaoh and her maids came to the river to wash. As she drew near, she saw the basket in the bulrushes and had it brought to her. Her delight on finding the baby inside was great to behold, even though she realised that it must be one of the forbidden children of Israel. Looking up she saw a young Israelite girl standing nearby – the sister of the baby, though Pharaoh's daughter did not know this, of course. The princess asked the girl to find an Israelite woman who could care for the baby until the child was old enough to live with the princess. The girl rushed off and brought back her mother – the baby's own mother. Pharaoh's daughter gave the baby to her and asked her to care for him. So it was that the child was first brought up by his own mother and then brought into the palace of Pharaoh where the princess named him, Moses, because she had taken him out of the water. Moses grew up in the court of the Pharaoh, and even though he was loved as a son by the princess, he knew that he was an Israelite.

2. *The Burning Bush*

The day came, when Moses had grown to be a man, when he wished to go and see his own people. He was deeply shocked to see the way in which they were treated and he grew angry in his heart. While walking one day he came upon an Egyptian beating one of the Israelites. Moses glanced around to make sure that no one could see him and then he struck the Egyptian down and buried his body in the sands. The very next day Moses came upon two Israelites fighting. Moses was shocked and tried to stop them. Whereupon one of the men said, "Are you going to kill us like you killed the Egyptian?" When Moses heard this he was very frightened. Obviously news of the murder had got out and it would be dangerous for him to stay in the land of Egypt. That very day he fled Egypt and went to the land of Midian.

Moses soon settled down in the land of Midian and married the daughter of a priest. But while Moses lived peacefully in Midian, the fortune of the Israelites grew worse and worse, until in their despair, they cried out to their God for help. And God heard their cry and remembered his people.

Back in Midian, Moses was out with a flock of sheep when he saw an extraordinary sight. There, on the hillside was a burning bush. Yet as Moses watched, he saw that the bush was not being destroyed by the fire. Fascinated by this burning bush which seemed not to burn, Moses moved closer to it. Then from the centre of the flame came the voice of God.

"Moses, Moses", said God.

"Here I am", said Moses.

"Come no nearer," said God, "but take off your shoes, for this is holy ground. I am the God of your father, the God of Abraham, Isaac and Jacob."

When Moses heard this he covered his face, afraid to look on God.

Then the voice came again: "I know of the sufferings of my people. I will deliver them from their slavery and bring them to a land flowing with all the good things of life – a land flowing with milk and honey. I have seen the terrible oppression of my people and I will now send you to Pharaoh to bring my people out of Egypt."

Moses was greatly frightened by this and said, "Who am I to do this task? Who shall I say has sent me? What name shall I give to you?"

Then God spoke again. "I Am who I Am. Tell them I Am has sent you."

God told Moses how things would occur. How Moses was to gather all the elders of the people together and explain what God intended doing. Then they were to go to Pharaoh and ask permission to go for three days into the wilderness to worship God. How Pharaoh would not listen and what mighty acts would then follow. And to help Moses in this great task, God told him that Aaron, Moses' brother, would also be there to help him, for Moses was very worried about this dangerous mission.

So Moses returned to Egypt to do the work of the Lord.

3. "Let My People Go!"

Just as God had foretold, Pharaoh would not listen to Moses when he asked for his people to be allowed to leave Egypt to worship God. Instead he made the life of the Israelites even worse than before. And Moses turned to God and asked why this should be happening. God told him that the time had come to punish Pharaoh and to force him to let the people of Israel go.

The next day, Moses confronted Pharaoh as he walked by the river. "You have not let my people go. To show you the power of our God I will strike the waters of the river and it will change into blood."

And it was so. For the river turned into blood and all life in it died. But Pharaoh was not impressed and turned away from Moses.

So for a second time, Moses came before Pharaoh, "Let my people go or God will plague this land with a swarm of frogs."

And again, Pharaoh ignored Moses, so God sent a terrible

plague of frogs. And Pharaoh called Moses and promised that if the plague was sent away, he would let the people go. But as soon as the frogs went, Pharaoh forgot his promise and ignored Moses again.

So God sent another plague, the third. And this time the country was covered by mosquitoes who swarmed everywhere. But Pharaoh still ignored Moses.

For a fourth time Moses spoke to Pharaoh, and warned him that the next plague would be a swarm of gadflies. Pharaoh did not believe him, until the very next day, he awoke to find gadflies everywhere. And Pharaoh agreed to let the people go, once the gadflies had gone. And yet again, as soon as the gadflies had gone, Pharaoh forgot his promise and ignored the cries of Moses for justice.

And a fifth time, God sent a plague. This time all the cattle belonging to the Egyptians were struck dead, while the flocks belonging to the Israelites were all right. But still Pharaoh ignored Moses' pleas.

A sixth time God sent a plague of boils which covered the bodies of the people of Egypt and their animals. But still Pharaoh refused to listen to Moses.

Now the seventh plague caused terrible destruction. For God sent thunder and lightning and vast storms of hail which slew all who stood in its way. Only in the areas where the Israelites lived did the storm not fall. And Pharaoh was truly frightened and begged Moses to stop the hail and storms. In return, Pharaoh agreed again to let the people go. So Moses went out and stopped the storm. And, yes, Pharaoh again betrayed Moses' trust. He refused to let the people of Israel go and worship their God.

Then Moses threatened a plague of locusts. And the advisers of the Pharaoh begged him to let the people go. So Pharaoh summoned Moses and asked who were to leave the country. When Moses said that all the people of Israel were to go, Pharaoh grew angry and forbad all the people to go. So Moses stretched forth his hands and the land was covered with locusts. When Pharaoh saw the terrible destruction these insects created he begged Moses to end the plague and promised to let all the people go. So once more Moses ended the plague, and yet again, Pharaoh ordered the Israelites to be kept in Egypt.

Then God turned the day into night and there was no light for three days. Pharaoh was now so frightened that he agreed that all the people of Israel could go to worship God, but that all their flocks and belongings were to be left in Egypt. Moses refused and Pharaoh's anger rose. "Do not come before me again", commanded Pharaoh, "or you will die."

Moses obeyed, but at the door he turned and said, "You have said it; never again shall I appear before you."

Then God sent the final and most awful plague. He decided to kill all the eldest sons of the Egyptians, and all the eldest offspring of the animals of the Egyptians. But God warned the Israelites. They were to take the blood of a lamb and mark the doors of their homes. Thus, as God passed throughout the land, he would not strike dead those in homes marked with the lamb's blood. God also commanded the Israelites to bake simple, unleavened bread which could be made and eaten quickly, for he knew that the people would have to move very quickly once the terrible tenth plague had fallen on Egypt.

And it happened as God had said. God passed over the country, and all the first born of the Egyptians died, but the children and flocks of the Israelites were spared. Finally, Pharaoh gave in and ordered all the Israelites, their flocks and their belongings to leave Egypt immediately. So the Israelites packed their belongings and took the unleavened bread to feed them, and the vast horde of them moved away to the border of Egypt, to go to the Promised Land. But Pharaoh was not yet done and his heart was still full of treachery.

4. Crossing the Sea

The people of Israel, freed from slavery in Egypt following the ten terrible plagues, made their way towards the border of Egypt. To lead them, God sent a pillar of cloud for the day-time, and at night, a pillar of fire.

But Pharaoh had changed his mind yet again, and he ordered his troops to hunt the Israelites down. By now the Israelites were moving along the coast of the Sea of Reeds – an easy target for the soldiers because there was no way of escape, except across the Sea, and the Israelites had no boats. So the army moved in for the kill.

When the people saw the Egyptian troops they were terrified. They began to panic and shouted at Moses that he and God had betrayed them. But Moses calmed them and turned to face the waters of the sea. Raising his staff in his hands, he pointed at the waters as God commanded him to do. To the amazement of the people, the waters began to roll back, until they had separated, to provide a dry crossing for the people. Moses led the people of God across the dry ground, with the waters held back on either side.

No sooner were they across than the Egyptian army, held back by the angel of God, began to advance onto the dry ground. The Israelites began to panic yet again, but Moses stretched forth his hands yet again, as God commanded, and the waters of the sea rolled back and destroyed the army of Pharaoh. At last, the people of Israel were out of Egypt and safe from the cruelty of Pharaoh.

Now began their long, long journey through the wilderness, towards the Promised Land of milk and honey.

5. Troubles on the Journey

Now life was hard in the wilderness. True, the people of Israel were no longer pursued by the Egyptians. But there was little to eat or drink and the people began to complain. "Have you brought us out here to die of starvation?" they asked Moses.

Then God spoke to Moses and told him that he would provide meat in the evening and bread in the morning to show God's glory. And sure enough, that evening, vast flocks of quails descended upon the camp of the Israelites. When morning came, the people found that the ground was covered in a strange powdery substance, which the people called 'manna'. Every morning, the manna lay upon the ground, and the people gathered it together. But if anyone tried to hoard the manna for the next day, it went bad and smelt terrible. Except for one day. On the Sabbath, when God forbade his people to work, there was no manna. But on the day before the Sabbath, the Lord provided twice as much, and it did not go rotten overnight. For all the forty years the Israelites were in the Wilderness, God provided manna for them.

6. *Mount Sinai*

The Israelites had been travelling through the wilderness for many months, when at last they came to Mount Sinai. Here they put up their tents and rested, while Moses went forward to the mountain to meet God. God spoke to Moses from the mountain: "Tell this to the people of Israel. You have seen how I brought you up out of the land of Egypt. You have seen how I cared for you. Now I will make a solemn agreement with you, a covenant between myself and you. If you listen to my voice and keep steadfastly to this agreement then I will be your God and you shall be my people."

So Moses returned to the camp, and summoning all the elders told them of God's promise. The elders all agreed that they would follow the way of God.

Moses then returned to the mountain, and God spoke again: "Tell the people that I am coming to them in a great thick cloud so that I may speak to them. They must prepare themselves. But when I descend on the mountain, they must not touch the mountain or they will surely die."

So Moses went and prepared the people for the coming of the Lord God.

It was on the third day that God descended upon the mountain. As the day broke, thunder roared and lightning flashed across the plain of Sinai. A vast cloud descended from the sky, the sound of trumpets rang out, and the people were truly afraid. But Moses led them forward to the foot of the mountain, and then he himself went into the cloud to meet God.

On the summit of the mountain God spoke to Moses and sealed the covenant with his people, the sons and daughters of Israel. And there on the mountain top God gave them the rules of the covenant, the rules which they must obey in all their lives. If the people followed these laws then he would protect them. There were many, many laws. The first ten were written in stone on two slabs.

Today those laws are known as the Ten Commandments.

But, sad to say, while Moses was upon the mountain top, the people began to get restless. They thought that Moses must have been taken away, he was so long. They began to regret trusting him and turned instead to their old, bad ways. Coming to Aaron, Moses' brother, they asked him to make them a statue of god they could see and follow. So Aaron, foolish Aaron, ordered all the gold in the camp to be melted down. From this he had the craftsmen cast a golden statue of a calf. "Here is the god who brought us out of Egypt", the people cried, and Aaron decided that the next day would be a feast day for this statue.

Meanwhile, God, having seen the way his people forgot their covenant, was moved to great anger. In his anger he turned to Moses and said: "Look how your people have deserted the true path. I shall destroy them all for their wickedness. You I will save, but they shall die."

But Moses pleaded with God to spare the people in honour of the ancient covenant with their forefathers, Abraham, Isaac and Jacob. And God relented and agreed not to destroy the people.

Then Moses descended from the mountain, and when he saw the idol which the people had made, his anger blazed forth like a terrible fire. Raising the two stone tablets above his head, he smashed them down upon the ground and broke them. Then he rushed forward and seized the golden calf and ground it to dust. He mixed the dust with water and made the people drink it.

But the people were out of hand, and rioting began to break out. Moses stood at the entrance to the camp and cried out, "Who is for God? To me!" The sons of the tribe of Levi ran to him and stood shoulder to shoulder. Then Moses commanded them to slay all those who were breaking the covenant of God, and the sons of the tribe of Levi took their swords and restored order to the people that day.

Then, when all was quiet, God called Moses onto the mountain once more and new tablets of stone were given to Moses.

At last Moses came down from the mountain. But Moses' face was so aglow, so radiant, that no one could look upon him until Moses had covered his face with a veil. And Moses at last gave the Laws to the people.

For forty years the people of Israel journeyed in the wilderness until they conquered and settled down in the land that God had promised them. Moses lived to be an old man of one hundred and twenty but he died before they reached their new land. All the

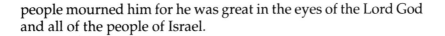

people mourned him for he was great in the eyes of the Lord God and all of the people of Israel.

Note:

This story can be told in conjunction with work on 'The 10 Commandments', in the *Junior Teacher's Handbook*, page 60. Further information on the Exodus, and the festival of Passover can be found on pages 6 & 93 of the *Infant Teacher's Handbook* and on pages 89-93 & page 128 of the *Junior Teacher's Handbook*.

Eli and Samuel

Hannah longed for a child. She was wretched because, although she loved her husband dearly, she had not been able to give him a son. So when she and her husband went to offer the yearly sacrifice, she stood in front of the altar of the Lord, praying desperately for a son.

"If you only grant me a son," she prayed, "I promise that I will bring him to the temple as soon as he is weaned, so that he can serve you, O God, all the days of his life."

Eli, the priest who was in charge of the temple, saw Hannah standing there. He saw her lips move, he saw her wild, despairing gestures, and he saw the tears rolling down her face. He thought she was drunk.

"You should be ashamed of yourself!" he said. "Appearing in the temple in this drunken state! Go and sober up!"

But Hannah turned to him, and said: "Do not think badly of me. Indeed I'm not drunk, but a woman in great distress. I was pouring out my soul to the Lord, and telling him of my grief and resentment."

Eli looked more closely, and he saw that what she said was true.

"Go in peace," he said, "and may the God of Israel grant what you have asked of him."

And so it was that soon after Hannah and her husband returned from the temple, she became pregnant and eventually gave birth to a son. She called him Samuel. She nursed him and took delight in him and watched him grow. But as soon as he was weaned, and no longer needed to drink her milk, she took him to Eli the priest, and explained the promise she had made to God.

"As you have promised, so let it be", said Eli. "Let the boy stay here with me, and I will look after him, and teach him how to serve the Lord God. You return home, and be at peace. And may God send you more children to take the place of this one you have given to him."

So Hannah went home, and once a year, when the time came to go and offer the sacrifice, she made a tunic for her son Samuel to wear, and took it to him at the temple. And Samuel grew in body and in mind, and Eli looked after him as if he was his son.

But Eli's own sons were a bitter disappointment to him. They too served in the temple, but they did not act honestly. They stole the food that people brought for sacrifice, and took by force any-thing else that they wanted. Eli tried to stop them, but he was old, and they took no notice. Besides, he was fond of them and did not want to be too harsh with them. People tried to tell him that he must put a stop to their evil ways.

"You and your sons were chosen to serve God in the Temple", they said. "Whatever it takes, you must stop them dishonouring God in this way. Otherwise you are giving more honour to your sons than to God!" But Eli could not bring himself to discipline his sons.

Now, as Eli got older and more feeble, it gradually came about that Samuel did more and more of the work to take care of the temple, and the altar of the Lord, and the flame that burnt in front of the altar. At night Samuel used to sleep in the temple to take care of the flame and make sure that it did not go out. One night, as he lay in the temple, Samuel heard a voice calling "Samuel, Samuel!"

At once he got up and ran to Eli's room, and said, "I'm here. What is it? Why did you call me?"

"I did not call you", said Eli. "Go back and lie down again."

So Samuel lay down again and went back to sleep. But again he heard the voice saying, "Samuel! Samuel!" And again he got up and ran to Eli.

"You called me", he said. "I'm here."

"No", said Eli, "I didn't call. Go back and lie down."

But no sooner was he lying down than he heard the voice a third time, "Samuel! Samuel!" and he ran to Eli again.

"You did call me!" he said. "What is it?"

Then Eli realised that God was calling to the boy, and wished to speak to him. "Go back again," he said, "and if you hear the voice again, say 'Speak, Lord. Your servant is listening'."

So again Samuel lay down once more. And at once God spoke to him again: "Samuel! Samuel!"

"Speak, Lord," said Samuel, "for your servant is listening."

God spoke to Samuel, and told him many things that were going to happen. And he gave Samuel a message for Eli.

In the morning, Samuel was afraid to give God's message to Eli, for it was a hard thing for a young boy to say to his teacher. But Eli called him. "Samuel, my son", he said. "What message did God give you last night?"

Samuel stood silent.

"Do not hide it from me", said Eli. "God will punish you if you do not speak his message exactly as he gave it to you."

So Samuel told him how God had rejected Eli's son's as priests. "They will all die, because you did not stop them from dishonouring God. And you will grow old and be left to mourn alone. This is what God told me to say."

There was a silence. Eli knew that Samuel had truly heard the voice of God. At last he forced himself to speak: "He is the Lord. Let him do what he thinks good." And he turned and stumbled into the temple.

Note:
This story can be told in conjunction with work on 'Learning from each other' in the *Junior Teacher's Handbook*, pages 39 & 40.

David the Shepherd Boy

L ong, long, ago in the land of Israel, there lived a prophet called Samuel. Many times Samuel had heard God speaking to him, and he always did what God told him.

Then one day he heard God say to him: "Go and visit a man

called Jesse, who lives in Bethlehem. One of his sons is the man I have chosen to be the next King of Israel. Go to his house, and I will tell you which one it is."

So Samuel set off and went to Jesse's house. Jesse brought in his sons to meet Samuel, one by one. When the first one came in, Samuel looked at him and thought, "He is tall and handsome. He looks strong and a good fighter – just what we need for a king!"

But God said to him, "Take no notice of what he looks like. You only see the outside of a person, but I am God, and I can see what his heart and mind are like. This is not the man I have chosen."

Then Jesse brought his second son in, and Samuel heard God say, "This is not the man I have chosen."

So Jesse brought his third son in, and Samuel heard God say, "This is not the man I have chosen."

Jesse brought in his fourth son, his fifth son, his sixth son, and his seventh son, one after the other, and each time Samuel heard God say, "This is not the man I have chosen."

Eventually Samuel said to Jesse, "Have you brought me all your sons?"

"Well," said Jesse, "there is the youngest, David. He is out looking after the sheep. But he is only a boy. He can't be the one you are looking for."

"Ask him to come in", said Samuel.

So Jesse sent a messenger out to the hills, where David was looking after the sheep. It was a lonely place, and David was often on his own there with the sheep. He spent his time singing and praying to God, and only God and the sheep knew what a fine singer he was. Sometimes wild animals attacked the sheep, and David had to fight them off. Only God and the sheep knew what a fine fighter David was. David only knew that God looked after him, and that made him so happy that he made up his own songs and sang them alone on the hillside.

It took a little while for Jesse's messenger to find David, but Samuel waited patiently. At last David came into the room. He looked very small beside his big strong brothers, but Samuel looked at his young face, and he heard God say, "This is the one I have chosen. Pour oil on him as a sign that he is to be king one day."

So Samuel took the jar of holy oil that he had brought with him, and poured it on David's head as a sign that God had chosen him.

Then Samuel went on his way, and David went back to his sheep. Everything seemed the same as before, but God knew that there were great things in store for young David, the shepherd boy.

And he did indeed become king, as God had promised – the greatest king that the Jewish people had ever had. But before that he had many more adventures.

David and Goliath

This is a story about the shepherd boy, David, who became the greatest king that the Jews ever had. Before he became king he had many adventures. This is a story of his most famous adventure.

Israel was at war with the Philistines. King Saul, the King of Israel, led his army out to meet the Philistine army. The Philistine army stood ready for battle on the hill on one side of a valley, and the Israelite army stood ready for battle on the hill on the other side of the valley. But they did not fight yet. Both sides waited to see what the other would do.

Then a man stepped forward from the Philistine army. His name was Goliath, and he was enormous! The Israelites had never seen anyone so big, so fierce, and so frightening. His body was covered with heavy armour, and he carried a spear and a sword. In a voice like thunder he shouted: "Listen, you Israelites, you slaves of King Saul! I am offering to fight any one of you to decide this battle. If your man wins, then we will all be your servants. But if I win, then you will be our servants. Now find someone who will fight with me, man to man!"

The Israelites looked at each other. No one wanted to fight Goliath, for they knew they would lose. So no one answered Goliath's call, and he went back into the Philistine camp. But the next day he came out, and shouted the same message, and the next day, and the next. Every day he came out and asked for one of the Israelites to fight him, and every day the Israelites gave no reply. Soon the Philistines began to laugh at them.

Now in the Israelite army there were three brothers, sons of a man called Jesse. One day Jesse sent his youngest son, David, to take some food to his brothers in the army, and to see how they were getting on. David arrived at the Israelite army just as Goliath was shouting his usual message.

"Just listen to that!" said David to his brothers. "Who does he think he is? Doesn't he know that God is fighting for us? Why has no one answered him yet?"

"Look at him, David", said his big brother. "He is so big and strong none of us could fight him and win. We'd all be killed!"

But David seemed unconcerned and asked, "Is there a reward for anyone who fights with Goliath and kills him?"

"Mind your own business!" said his brother. "You've left your sheep all alone at home, why don't you get back to them. This is work for men, not little boys! You only came to see us so you could watch the battle!"

But David went on asking about Goliath, and wondering why no one would fight him. At last King Saul heard about him, and sent for him.

"What is this I am hearing about you?" said King Saul.

"It's simple, your Majesty", said David. "I will fight Goliath for you. God will help me, and I will beat him."

"But you are only a boy, and the bravest men in my army are afraid of Goliath!" said King Saul.

"Your majesty, when I am out looking after my father's sheep, there are sometimes lions and bears who come and try to take a lamb from the flock. I fight them, and I have killed lions and bears before, so why not Goliath? God helps me and gives me strength."

"Very well," said King Saul, "you may go and fight Goliath. But take my sword and my armour to protect you." So they brought King Saul's great bronze sword, and the heavy armour to put on. But when David put the armour on, and tried to lift the king's great sword he found he could not move. They were so heavy! So he took them off, and went out just as he was, in his shepherd's clothes. He went to the stream and chose five small, round stones that fitted in his sling. Then he went forward to meet Goliath.

When Goliath first saw David coming towards him he laughed, but then he also began to get angry. "How dare you send a young boy against me!" he shouted. "Are you laughing at me? I am the greatest fighter in the world! Come here you puny boy, and I will kill you!"

"O no," said David, "it is you who will be killed. You have laughed at my people and laughed at my God, and my God has sent me to kill you."

David put one of his stones into his sling, whirled it round his head, and let go. Straight and true, the stone flew through the air, and before Goliath knew what was happening, the stone hit him on the head and he fell forward on his face. David ran forward, took Goliath's sword, and cut off his head.

The Israelites cheered when they saw what had happened, but the Philistines turned and ran. The Israelites drew their swords and chased after them, and many Philistines were killed and wounded that day, as the Israelite army chased the Philistines far away, back to their own land.

Then they returned to their camp and gave thanks to God, and to David, the boy who had saved them with only his sling and his faith that God would help him.

Solomon the Wise

T here is a saying which goes: "Some are born great, some achieve greatness, and some have greatness thrust upon them."

Solomon was born great for he was the son of a king, but he also achieved greatness because of his wisdom. He was known as Solomon the Wise throughout the ancient world, as his father had been known as David, the giant killer.

Solomon became king of Israel while still a young man. He loved God and he loved his people and he wanted to serve both as well as he could. But he was troubled. He wasn't frightened about commanding the army or building a strong city. He wasn't worried about organizing the officials in the land. He was troubled because in those days part of the task of being king was to be a judge. A man arguing with his neighbour about who owned the land would come to the king and ask for his judgement. Two women quarrelling about a just price for some cloth would come to the king for judgement. Serious cases and trivial came before the king.

Solomon wondered how he could make such judgements. He didn't know each one individually. He didn't know how he would be able to tell who was right and who was wrong.

Then one night he had a dream. He dreamt that God came to him and said, "Ask what you would like me to give you." And in his dream Solomon replied, "I am still a very young man, and I don't know how to be a leader. Give me a heart that will understand how to judge between good and evil so that I can govern my people wisely."

And God was pleased with Solomon for his request, because he hadn't asked for wealth or the death of his enemies but had thought only of serving his people. So God said, "I will give you a heart which is wise and shrewd. No one has ever been as wise as you will be, and there will never be anyone so wise again."

Solomon awoke from his dream and praised God.

The next day two women came and stood before the king. One said: "If it please your Lordship, I live in the same house as this woman. We have both just had babies. One morning I woke to feed my baby but he was gone. There lying next to me was a dead baby, but he wasn't mine. No, my Lord he was this woman's baby. He had died in the night. She crept in and took my son from me and put her own dead child in his place. My Lord, I want my son back, please."

But the other woman cried out: "She is lying my Lord. It is my son who is alive. It is her son who is dead", and the two began to argue before the king.

Each onlooker asked himself how the king would make his judgements because nobody else had been in the house. Nobody else had witnessed the birth and could say to whom the child belonged. There seemed to be no solution to the problem.

But then King Solomon spoke. "Bring me a sword", he demanded.

Everyone looked at each other. Why would the king want a sword?

"Cut the baby in half", commanded the king. "Give one half to one woman and the other half to the other."

One woman paled but she said, "Yes, that is fair. He shall belong to neither of us. Cut him up."

But the other was in anguish for the baby. "No, no, do not cut him in half! If it pleases your Lord, let her have the child."

Then Solomon made his decision. "Give the child to the mother who would let him go rather than see him killed. She truly is his mother."

Jcc '95

The Story of Hanukah

Alexander the Great, the mighty king of Macedonia, conquered many parts of the ancient world. His rule stretched north and south, east and west. His empire also included the little country of Israel. Alexander was a powerful and wise ruler. He treated his subjects well, and allowed them to follow their own religions, so the great Temple in Jerusalem, where the Jews worshipped, was safe. But after Alexander died, quarrelling broke out in the areas he had ruled, and mighty armies fought over each small country.

After bitter struggles, Israel was taken over by the powerful country of Syria. For many years they were treated well, but then a new king came to the throne of Syria. He was a Greek, and followed the Greek gods, but he also believed that he was a god himself, and wanted everyone to worship him.

So he issued new laws.

"The Jews have been keeping the Sabbath as a holy day of rest and rejoicing", he declared. "This must stop immediately."

"No one must read the Jewish holy book, the Torah."

"The Jews have to eat the same food as everyone else. How dare they follow their own rules – it is MY rule which counts."

"Everyone must bow down and worship the Greek gods. Anyone who does not is a traitor."

Word of these laws spread quickly through Israel, and the Jews looked at each other in horror and fear. How could they obey them? The very first command that God had given them was, "You shall have no other Gods but me."

God had also told them, "Remember the Sabbath day to keep it holy."

What would become of them if they obeyed a mere man, rather than their one true God? But what would become of them if they ignored the laws of such a mighty king, especially a king such as this one, who was known for his cruelty?

In those hard and bitter times, each Jew had a terrible decision to make. Some refused to obey the new laws, and were cruelly put to death. Others, seeing the fate of their countrymen, did as they were ordered, sick at heart.

But the horror did not end there. Even worse things were in store for the Jewish people. Their greatest and holiest building was the temple in Jerusalem. The first temple had been built hundreds of years before by the great King Solomon, and God had promised that, whenever the Jewish people prayed to him in the temple, he would be there and would hear them. The first temple had been destroyed by an invading army, but the Jews had worked and struggled to rebuild it, and the new temple had been as precious to them as the old one.

Now the Syrian army invaded the temple, this most holy of holy places. They put up statues of the Greek gods and demanded that the people worship them. On the great altar, pigs, to Jews the most unclean of all animals, were sacrificed and their blood sprinkled in the most holy parts of the temple.

At last, a small group of Jews could bear it no longer. Under the leadership of Judah Maccabee, they took to the wild inaccessible hillsides and began to attack the Syrian armies. They were only a small band, but they knew the country well, and they had the support of the people. Little by little, the Syrian army was driven back, and the Jewish army grew strong as more people came to join them. Even when the Syrians attacked them with elephants they did not flinch.

After a long and bloody struggle, the Syrians were defeated, and the victorious army of Judah Maccabee entered Jerusalem rejoicing. Once again the temple was in Jewish hands.

But what a sight met their eyes! It was even worse than they had feared. The Syrians had deliberately spoilt and broken everything they could lay their hands on. Not only were there statues of Greek gods in their temple, but the precious scrolls on which

God's Law was written were ripped to pieces and scattered on the floor. And every corner of the temple was splattered with pigs blood.

Shocked and sickened, the people began the task of clearing up. Everywhere had to be cleaned and scrubbed to remove all trace of what the Syrians had done. When the temple was completely clean it was ready to be re-dedicated to God. The lamp which always burned before the altar could now be re-lit as a sign of God's presence in the temple.

But now a new difficulty arose.

"Where is the holy oil for the lamp?"

"There is none – the Syrians smashed and spoiled the jars, and there has been no one to make new oil."

"How long will it take to make new oil?"

"Eight days – can we wait until it is ready?"

"Eight days! That is far too long! We must start the worship of God here immediately, especially as tomorrow is the anniversary of the day the Syrians first invaded the temple and defiled it. Is there no oil at all?"

"Well – there is this tiny flask we found, rolled behind one of those dreadful statues, but sealed and unbroken. But it's nowhere near enough. It'll barely last one day, let alone eight."

"Never mind. We must light the lamp and dedicate the temple tomorrow. Start work on the new oil straight away, and if the lamp goes out meanwhile, God will know the reason and forgive us."

So with rejoicing and prayers to God, the lamp was lit and the temple was re-dedicated. The people joyfully carried branches, leafy boughs and palms, and offered hymns to God. It was God who had brought them back to Jerusalem, and it was God who had given them the strength to restore the temple. And as they celebrated day after day, a great miracle happened. The lamp, which had only had enough oil to last for one day, did not go out. It took eight days for the new oil to arrive, but for eight days the lamp stayed alight, shining out to show that God had returned to his chosen place.

So the Jewish people decided that, from then on, this festival would be kept for eight days, to remember what God had done for them. The festival is called Hanukah, which means 'dedication', and Jews light special candles, one on the first day of the festival, two on the second, and so on, to commemorate their deliverance from the cruel king, and the miracle of the temple lamp.

Note:
This story can be told in conjunction with work on 'Lights at Hanukah' in the *Junior Teacher's Handbook*, page 83. Further material on Hanukah can be found on pages 7 & 93 of the *Infant Teacher's Handbook* and pages 8, 83 & 128 of the *Junior Teacher's Handbook*.

—◁□▷—

Esther the Jewish Queen

King Ahasuerus was king of Persia, and emperor of vast lands to east and west. He ruled over lands from India to Ethiopia, and over people of hundreds of different races and faiths. He ruled in the city of Susa, and among his officials there was a Jew called Mordecai. Mordecai had a niece, whose name was Esther. Her mother and father had died, and Mordecai had brought her up, and adopted her as his daughter. Esther was so beautiful that it seemed all who saw her loved her.

In the third year of his reign, King Ahasuerus quarrelled with his wife, the queen, because she had refused to obey an order he had sent her. To punish her, he resolved that she would no longer be queen, and he would never set eyes on her again. Instead, he ordered that all the most beautiful women in his empire were to be brought to the palace and given rooms in his harem. They would all be his wives, and the one who pleased him most would be his new queen.

So Esther, along with hundreds of other beautiful women, was taken to the palace. There they were made comfortable, and given anything they needed to make themselves attractive to the king – beauty treatments, jewellery, and fine clothes.

Now Esther was living in great comfort and luxury, but she never forgot her uncle. Every day he would walk outside the palace, and she would come out on the balcony, so that he could see that all was well with her.

One by one, the women were taken to the king, but none of

them pleased him enough for him to ask to see her again. Each one tried to win his favour by taking gifts with her to the king.

When it was Esther's turn, she prepared herself carefully, but she took nothing with her. And so it was that it was simply as herself that she won the king's favour, and not by means of any gifts. He put the royal diadem on her head and proclaimed her queen. Now she had her own apartments and her own servants and had to obey no one but the king.

Mordecai, meanwhile, continued to serve the king faithfully. He worked in the chancellery of King Ahasuerus, where the king's commands were prepared for sending out to all the different parts of the empire. One day he found out that two of the king's officers were planning to kill him and take his kingdom. Mordecai immediately sent a message to his niece Esther, and she told the king. The two men were arrested and executed, and the king became even more fond of his queen Esther.

At about this time, the king put a new man in charge of the chancellery. His name was Haman, and he thought very well of himself. So well, in fact, that he thought everyone in the chancellery should stand up and bow down to the ground whenever he came near. And because Haman was the king's chief official, his commands had the same force as commands from the king. This made a problem for Mordecai.

"I cannot bow down to a man!" he thought to himself. "I only bow before God, and I cannot give a man the same honour I give to God."

So whenever Haman was near, Mordecai tried to keep himself in the background, so that Haman would not notice that he was not bowing down. The other officials asked him, "Why do you flout the royal command?", but Mordecai did not answer. So eventually they reported him to Haman.

Haman was furious. "How dare he treat me with disrespect!" he shouted. "Killing him is not good enough! I'll... I'll... I know what I'll do! I'll kill all his people as well as Mordecai! Not a Jew will remain alive in this kingdom!"

So Haman went to the king, and said to him: "Did you know, O King, that there is a race of people in your kingdom who have their own laws and their own outlandish customs? They think they are above our laws, and it will soon lead to sedition and treason. You had better kill them all now, before there's any trouble."

"Is that so?" said the king. "Yes, you had better see to it. Cast lots for the right day to perform the executions, and send out the orders to all my lands."

So Haman cast lots to see what day would seal the fate of the Jews, and sent out orders to every governor of every province in the empire, that in the name of good government and the peace of the king's domains, all Jews, men, women and children, were to be killed on the thirteenth day of the twelfth month.

What consternation reigned throughout the land when the Jews heard this law! And how much worse it was for Mordecai, who realised that it was through his action that this dreadful thing had come about! He tore his clothes, he put on sackcloth and ashes, the signs of mourning, and he ran through the streets crying aloud in his despair. But then he had an idea. Perhaps all might not be lost, for was not his own niece the queen, to whom the king showed great favour? At once he sent a message to Esther, giving her a copy of Haman's order, and asking her to go to the king and plead with him for her people.

"Do not forget your humble origins," he said, "and how I fed you and looked after you when you were little. Pray to the Lord, speak to the king, and save us from death!"

When Esther heard this message she was greatly distressed. "How can I do it?" she said. "All the king's servants know that no one is allowed to enter his presence unless he has asked for them. The penalty for doing so is death. And the king has not sent for me for the last thirty days."

The messenger came back and told this to Mordecai. "Tell her this:" replied Mordecai, "do you think that you will escape this law? You too are a Jew. Even if God saves the Jewish race, you and your family are bound to perish. Who knows, maybe it was for this that God gave you your beauty, and caused you to find favour with the king. Maybe you are meant to be the saviour of your people."

So Esther sent back this message: "Tell all the Jews in Susa to pray and fast for me. Do not eat or drink anything for three days. I and my maids will do the same. After the three days I will go to the king in spite of the law, and if I perish, I perish."

So the Jews outside the palace, and Queen Esther and her maids within, put on sackcloth and ashes, and neither ate nor drank.

Mordecai prayed to God, and said: "O Lord, hear my prayer. Have mercy on your people, and turn our grief into rejoicing, that we may live to praise your name. Do not allow the mouths of those who praise you to be silenced."

And inside the palace, Esther prayed. "O my Lord, our King, the only one, come to my help, for I am alone and have no helper but you, and am about to take my life in my hands. Give me courage, put persuasive words into my mouth when I face the king."

On the third day Esther took off her sackcloth clothes, and put on once again the full finery of a queen. She combed her hair into a regal style, and she put on her jewels. Her maids gathered round her as she prepared to go to the king. But when she stood up, she found that she was so weak from the fasting, and her heart beat so fast from fear, that she could hardly walk. So she leaned on one of her maids, trying to make it look as though it was simply a casual gesture, and another maid gathered up her train behind.

And so, dazzling with beauty but palpitating with fear, Queen Esther made her way through the palace to the king's hall. He sat there with his ministers of state, dressed in golden robes, and glittering with precious stones. He looked up, and his face blazed with anger. At the sight of this, Esther's small remaining strength deserted her. Her face went deathly white, and she sank to the ground.

But when the king saw his beloved queen look so ill, his heart was softened. He sprang from his throne and took her in his arms.

"Do not look so frightened, my love", he cried. "Do not faint, take heart. You may come and speak to me. My order only applies to ordinary people. What is it you want? Only tell me, even if it is half my kingdom, and it is yours."

And Esther replied, in a faltering voice, "Please, my king, will you come to the banquet I have prepared, and bring Haman with you?"

"Send for Haman, quickly," ordered the king, "and bring him here to me, that Queen Esther may have her wish."

So they went to the banquet, and as they drank their wine, the king again asked Esther what it was she wanted from him.

"If I have found favour with you, O king," she said, "then come again to my banquet tomorrow, and again bring Haman with you. Then I will tell you what is on my mind."

Haman went home that day in great excitement. "There is no one like me", he boasted to his wife. "Not only has the king honoured me, but Queen Esther herself invited me to a banquet today, and wants me to go back tomorrow. But it was all spoilt", he shouted, his face twisting with rage, "when I saw that Jew Mordecai. He still refuses to bow down to me! I will have a scaffold built this very day, ready to hang him on!"

That night, the king could not sleep. To pass the time, he sent for the book in which were written all the events of his reign, and amused himself by reading about the great things he had done. And there he read again how Mordecai the Jew had uncovered the plot to kill him, and had given him warning.

"Was any reward or honour given to Mordecai for this?" he asked his courtiers.

"No, O king, nothing was done for him", they replied.

"Which of my ministers is on duty outside?" asked the king.

Now it so happened that Haman had just arrived outside the king's rooms, to ask to have Mordecai hanged on the gallows he had just put up. So the courtiers told the king that Haman was there.

"Bring him in", said the king. As soon as Haman came in, the king asked him, "What should be done for a man whom the king wishes to honour?"

Greatly excited, Haman thought to himself, "He must mean me! Who else would he wish to honour?" So he replied: "He should be given royal robes to wear, robes which the king has worn, and a horse which the king has ridden. A crown should be put on his head, and one of the king's officers would lead him through the streets, proclaiming 'This is how the king treats a man he wishes to honour!'"

"Very good!" said the king. "Go now, quickly, and do all that you have said to Mordecai the Jew, who works at the chancellery."

Gnashing his teeth and almost bursting with suppressed anger, Haman went and did as the king told him, and led Mordecai through the streets on horseback, proclaiming that the king was honouring him. He had no sooner returned home to hide his outraged feelings, than the king's messenger arrived to take him to Queen Esther's banquet.

Once again they sat feasting, and once again the king sat drinking his wine.

"Tell me your request, my queen," said the king, "and I promise you shall have it, even if it is half my kingdom."

"If I have found favour with you, if ever I have pleased you, O king," replied Esther, "grant me my life!"

The king stared at her in astonishment.

"My life, and the life of my people," went on Esther, "for we are doomed to death. Do you not know what a loss your kingdom is about to sustain, if you let this thing happen?"

"Who is doing this?" roared the king. "Who is the schemer of such an outrage?"

"He is here, in your presence. This wretch, Haman, formed this plan to destroy my people, the Jews."

At this the king rose in a rage. "He has built a scaffold for execution!" he cried. "Let us make use of it! Hang him immediately!"

When the king learnt of all that had happened, he gave all Haman's house and riches to Esther, and he gave Haman's job and the honour that went with it to Mordecai. "You have my authority and my seal", he said. "Any orders that you give in my name will be my orders, unchangeable. Write quickly to the governors of the provinces that on no account are they to harm any of your people, the Jews, and that the order to kill them is revoked. And you and your people shall live with honour in my kingdom."

Every year Jews remember the faithfulness of Mordecai and the bravery of Esther. They call the festival Purim, which means 'lots', because Haman cast lots to find the day on which the Jews should die. Before the day they fast, just as Esther and the Jews fasted. At the festival, the scroll telling the story of Esther is read aloud in the synagogue, and every time the name of 'Haman' is mentioned, everyone makes as much noise as they can, booing, shouting, banging tin trays, and blowing hooters, to drown out the name of the wicked man who tried to destroy the Jews.

Note:
Further information on Purim can be found on pages 6 & 93-94 of the *Infant Teacher's Handbook* and on page 128 of the *Junior Teacher's Handbook*.

The Story of Jonah

There was once a great city called Nineveh. The people there were very wicked. They were doing so many evil things that God decided that they needed to be punished. He told a man named Jonah to go to Nineveh and to tell the people there how wicked they were being.

Jonah wasn't pleased about this. He didn't want to go to Nineveh. In fact, he went down to the harbour and got on to a ship that was going somewhere completely different. He thought by doing that he could avoid doing what God had asked him to do.

Running away didn't do Jonah much good. When the boat was out at sea a great storm began: a terrible wind sprang up, the ship was tossed from side to side, and everyone was terrified. They believed that the ship would sink at any minute.

The sailors guessed that the storm was because someone had done something wrong. Soon they found out that Jonah was running away: he was running away from God.

They asked Jonah what they should do. Jonah knew that the storm was his fault, and so he told the sailors to take him and throw him into the sea.

Because the sailors did not want to do this, they tried as hard as they could to row the boat to land. It was no use. The storm was as bad as ever, and at any time they would sink. It was a dreadful thing to have to throw a man into the sea, but if they did not they would all die.

So Jonah was thrown into the stormy waters. When he was off the ship the sea became calm again, and the wind was gentle once more. The sailors were thankful because the storm had ended and they prayed to God to thank him.

Meanwhile Jonah was in even more trouble: one minute he had been fighting against the cold, cruel waves; the next, he was in the dark inside of a giant whale – swallowed alive!

He stayed inside the whale for quite a long time – three whole days and nights – and by this time he was very sorry that he had not listened to God. He prayed to God to help him, and promised that he would do as he had been told. God answered Jonah's prayer, and the whale threw Jonah out onto dry land.

Then God spoke to Jonah again and said, "Go to Nineveh. Preach the words that I have told you." This time Jonah listened to God – he went to Nineveh. When he arrived there he began to preach. He told the people of Nineveh that in forty days God would destroy their city because they were so wicked. The people were shocked. This message had frightened them, because they had not realized how angry God was. They dressed themselves in rough clothes and sat in ashes; none of them ate or drank anything. They did this to show God how sorry they were for what they had done. And when God saw this he decided that he would not destroy the people of Nineveh.

The people of Nineveh were happy to be spared, but Jonah was very angry. He had had all this trouble and come all this way to tell the people of Nineveh that they would be destroyed, and now God was sparing them!

Annoyed, Jonah left the city. It was a very hot day, and so he sat under a tree. The tree gave him shade from the heat of the sun, and this cheered him up a little.

Gradually, the day wore on, and Jonah fell asleep under the shade of the tree. But, when he awoke in the morning he found to his horror that during the night a worm had got into the tree trunk. The worm had eaten into the trunk and killed the tree.

The tree no longer gave him shade. The sun beat down on Jonah's head until he was faint. How he wished the tree was still there! He felt really miserable.

Then God spoke to Jonah. He said, "Are you angry about the tree?"

Jonah said that he was. God pointed out that Jonah hadn't had to work for the tree. He hadn't helped it to grow, and yet he would have wanted God to spare it. How much more important it was for God to spare the great city of Nineveh, which had many thousands of people in it.

Note:
This story can be told in conjunction with work on 'Breaking the law and forgiveness', in the *Junior Teacher's Handbook*, page 63.

Elijah and the Drought

Elijah was a great prophet in the land of Israel. When God had a message for the people, he spoke to Elijah, and Elijah told the people what God said. But not everybody listened. King Ahab, the king of Israel, took no notice of what God said. He was a bad king, and treated the people badly.

So God sent a terrible message. He said to Elijah, "Tell the king that there will be no rain in the land of Israel until I say the rain shall fall."

Elijah told the king this, and the king was very angry. So God told Elijah, "Go away all by yourself to a lonely valley. I will show you where to go. You can drink water from the stream there. I have told the ravens to bring you food."

So Elijah set off, all by himself, and found the valley. He stayed there alone for a long time. And every morning the ravens flew into the valley with bread in their strong black beaks, and gave it to Elijah. Every evening they came with meat, and gave it to Elijah.

And so Elijah lived in the valley, all on his own, with the ravens to look after him.

After some time the stream dried up, because there was no rain, and God spoke again to Elijah. "Go and stay at a place called Zarephath. There is a widow there who will look after you."

So Elijah went to Zarephath and came to the gate of the city. There was a widow gathering sticks. "Could you give me a little drink of water?" said Elijah.

"Yes, gladly", said the widow, and set off to her house to fetch it.

"Oh, and a bit of bread as well, please", said Elijah.

Sadly the widow replied: "I have only got a handful of flour in a barrel and little oil in a jar. I am gathering some fire wood to go and cook it for myself and my son, so that we can eat it. After that we will die of hunger."

Elijah told her: "Don't be afraid, go and do what you have said, but make me a little cake of it first and bring it to me, and afterwards make food for yourself and for your son. For God says to you the barrel of flour will not run out and neither will the jar of oil, until God sends rain on the earth."

The widow went and did what Elijah had told her, and to her amazement, it was so! Just as Elijah had said, the flour and the oil never ran out. Each time she thought that it was finished, she discovered just enough for that day's food. The widow and Elijah and her son ate for many days from the handful of flour and the small amount of oil in the jar, until at last God sent rain to the thirsty land.

Elijah and the Prophets of Baal

There was once an evil king in Israel, whose name was Ahab. He had killed many of God's prophets, and encouraged the Israelites to worship a god called Baal. Ahab's worst enemy was a prophet named Elijah, who wanted the Israelites to stop worshipping Baal and worship the Lord God of the Israelites again.

One day Elijah sent for Ahab. When the King came to him, he said, "It is time we saw which is the true God. Call all the people of Israel together to Mount Carmel, and bring all the prophets of Baal there too."

When everyone was gathered at Mount Carmel, Elijah told the Israelites, "You ought to make up your minds whom to follow. If the Lord is the true God, follow him; if Baal is the true god, then follow him."

Everyone was quiet, waiting for what he would say next.

Elijah suggested a test. "There are 450 prophets of Baal here, and I am the only prophet of the Lord left. I will prepare a sacrifice to my God: let the prophets of Baal prepare a sacrifice to their god. We will each put a bullock on an altar, but will not light the fire. The true God will show himself by lighting the fire under his sacrifice."

The prophets of Baal agreed to this, and prepared their altar first. They built it up with stones, and put wood and the body of a bullock on it. Then they began to pray to Baal. All morning they prayed and prayed; they danced around the altar, calling out, "Baal, hear us", but nothing happened.

They kept on praying till noon and soon people began to get bored since nothing was happening, and Elijah started making fun of the prophets. "Shout a bit louder. Perhaps Baal is busy talking. He might have gone hunting, or gone away on holiday. Maybe he is asleep – you'd better wake him up!"

The prophets of Baal got more and more desperate. They called out even louder, and started cutting themselves with knives until the blood was running down their bodies. And, although they carried on like this until evening, there was still no answer.

At last, it was Elijah's turn. He called all the Israelites to him, and repaired the Lord's altar, which had been broken down. He dug a deep trench around the altar. Then, when he had put the wood and the bullock on the altar, he told the people to pour four barrels of water over it. This must have seemed strange to them – after all, Elijah wanted the sacrifice to burn, didn't he?

But one lot of water wasn't enough for Elijah. He told them to do it again, and then yet again, until the wood was soaked, and the trench around the altar was full of water.

When he had done all this, Elijah began to pray. He didn't shout, or dance, or cut himself. He simply asked the Lord to show that He was really the true God, so that the Israelites would believe. When Elijah had finished his prayer, something astonishing happened. Fire came down from heaven and burned up the sacrifice. Not only that, it burned up the wood, the stones of the altar, and even the water in the trench! When the people realised that the prophets of Baal had been fooling them all this time, they took every single one of them and killed them; Elijah had shown them who the true God was.

Elijah and His Mantle

E lijah was a great prophet in Israel. For many years he had spoken God's message to the people, enduring many hardships and even, on occasion, facing the anger of the king. Now, one day God spoke to Elijah. God told him that his time on earth was coming to an end, and asked him to journey to Bethel. So Elijah set out from Gilgal, the place where he had been staying, and his disciple Elisha went with him. Elijah tried to stop Elisha from following him saying: "Stay here, for God has sent me as far as Bethel". But Elisha insisted on staying with Elijah, so they went to Bethel together.

In Bethel, the sons of the prophets came out to see Elijah, and said to Elisha, "Do you know that God will take your master away from you today?"

And Elisha answered, "Yes, I know. Be quiet."

After they had been in Bethel for some time Elijah took Elisha to one side and told him, "Stay here, for God has sent me to Jericho", but Elisha still refused to leave the prophet. So they went on to Jericho together.

In Jericho the sons of the prophets came out to see Elijah, and said to Elisha,"Do you know that God will take your master away from you today?"

And Elisha answered, "Yes, I know. Be quiet."

After a while, Elijah once more took his disciple to one side and told him, "Stay here, for God has sent me to Jordan", but Elisha still refused to leave the prophet, and they journeyed on to Jordan together.

When they got to the River Jordan, Elijah took off his cloak and hit the waters with it. Instantly the waters were divided so that he and his disciple Elisha could walk across on dry ground. When they had crossed the river, Elijah said to Elisha, "What shall I do for you, before I am taken away?"

And Elisha answered, "I pray you, let a double portion of your spirit come to me."

Elijah answered, "You have asked for something difficult, but if you see me when I am taken away, it shall be so. If you do not, then it shall not be so."

They carried on walking together and talking. Then suddenly there appeared a chariot of fire and horses of fire which came between them, and Elijah was taken up into heaven in a whirlwind. As Elisha stood watching in astonishment he saw the prophet's cloak fall from him. At once Elisha picked up the cloak and went back and stood by the bank of River Jordan. Once he had reached the river bank he took Elijah's cloak and struck the waters with it, as Elijah had done earlier. And, as before, the waters parted and Elisha walked over.

When the sons of the prophets saw him, they said that the spirit of Elijah rested on Elisha like the cloak itself, and they bowed to the ground before him.

⫸▢⫷

12/01 MSO

The Coins of Elijah

There are many stories of how the prophet Elijah has visited people on earth since he was taken up to heaven. This is one of them.

L ong ago there was a very good man who was always ready to help anyone who needed his help. He ran a successful business. If anyone needed money, he was always willing to give it to them. Then suddenly things began to go badly for him; his business started losing money; he was forced to work in the fields for his living. Yet still he would always give anything he could spare from his wages to anyone who really needed it.

One day, when he was working in the fields, a stranger came up to him. "Peace be to you and to your household", said the stranger.

"And peace be to you."

"I have come to tell you that you will get your fortune back and live in peace and prosperity for six years. You may choose whether this happens now or later on in your life. Which will it be?"

At first the man did not believe the stranger. What he said seemed very unlikely. He thanked the stranger for his good wishes and then carried on working in the fields. Then the stranger came back and again made the offer of wealth. Again, the man did not believe him. When the stranger came back for the third time, the man thought: "Well, it may be true. Let me go back and ask my wife about this", he said.

He ran off home as fast as he could and as soon as he arrived he told his wife what the stranger had said. "If this is really true, what shall we do? Shall we be wealthy now or later?"

"Oh, now", said his wife.

The man went back to the field and found the stranger still standing there. He told him what he and his wife had decided. The stranger then took two silver coins out of his pouch and gave them to the man. He said, "I'll come back in six years. Don't forget then to return what I have given you." The man took the coins and thanked the stranger. He promised that he would return the gift in six years. When he had done this, the stranger disappeared. There was no trace of him to be seen.

As soon as the man put the silver coins into his pocket, he felt better than he had done for a long time. He had a strange feeling, as if he knew deep inside him that he was soon to be very wealthy.

The very next day, as his son was digging near the house, he found a hidden treasure, a vast number of gold coins. He cried out in the excitement and soon the whole family came running to see what had happened. At once, they all thanked God for their new-found wealth.

The man's wife reminded him that they were only to be wealthy for six years. She said that while they were wealthy, they should put that money to good use. They should use it feed the hungry, clothe the poor and help those who had no one to depend on. That way, even when the wealth had gone, they would have the pleasure of knowing that they had helped so many people.

The family kept careful accounts of how much money they had spent, both on themselves and on other people. Every day, they managed to help someone new. They were so busy with this good work that six years passed very quickly.

When the six years were up, the stranger reappeared to them. He asked them to return their gift. The wife said, "Of course, but see first what we have done with it." She showed him the account books, so that he could see for himself how they had helped so many people.

The wife then said, "We will of course return your gift if you think we should. If you think that anyone would look after it better than we have, then take it away, but if you feel that we have done what was right with the money, then let us carry on looking after it."

The stranger now told them that he was the prophet Elijah. He blessed the family and told them that he could think of no one better to leave the money with, so he entrusted it to them for the rest of their lives. They continued to use their gift wisely and well and to be very happy.

Tales from the Sikhs

Guru Nanak

This is the story of how the Sikh faith started.

A long while ago in India, a little girl sat with her father outside her house. Her name was Nanaki, and inside the house, her mother was going to have a baby. Nanaki sat and waited, and listened.

"When I hear a baby cry," she said, "I will know that I have a new baby brother or sister."

After a little while the woman who was helping her mother have the baby came out of the house.

"Nanaki," she said, "it's a boy! You have a new baby brother."

"But I didn't hear any crying", said Nanaki.

"No," said the woman, "he is not like any other baby I have ever seen. Most babies cry when they are born, but this child just smiled. Even now, he has such a wise smile on his face, it makes me feel happy just to look at him."

Nanaki and her father held hands, and together they went into the house to look at the new baby.

"Oh!" said Nanaki. "He is beautiful! I know I shall love him and do what he wants all my life!"

"We shall call him Nanak", said her mother and father.

The next thing to do was to ask a wise man to study the stars at the time that baby Nanak had been born, to find out what sort of life he would have. Everyone in India did this when a baby was born. The man came, and Nanak's mother and father told him the exact time the baby had been born. He looked in his books, and he drew some patterns, and he thought very hard. At last he said: "This is wonderful. Your baby Nanak is going to be someone very special indeed. He will praise God and he will teach other people to praise God."

As baby Nanak began to grow up, Nanaki could see that she did indeed have a very special brother. He was very strong, and often helped her to carry things when she was helping her mother in the house. And he was very clever. When the time came for him to go to school, he went for a few days, and then the teacher came to his mother and father, and said, "I cannot teach your boy any more!"

"Why not?" they asked.

"Because he has already learnt everything I have to teach him. Now I am learning things from him!"

When he grew up, Nanak left home and got a good job but he still spent a lot of time singing hymns, meditating and thinking about God.

Then one day Nanak went down to the river to bathe before saying his prayers. He did not return. His clothes were found on the river bank, but there was no sign of Nanak. His friends looked everywhere for him. They feared that he had drowned. Three days later, Nanak did return.

"Where have you been? What happened to you?" his friends demanded.

All Nanak answered was, "There is neither Hindu nor Muslim." He said that God was not a Hindu, nor was he a Muslim. He was just God, and if people would only listen to him, God himself would teach them.

Now Nanak knew what God wanted him to do in his life. He knew he must travel to many places and teach people what he had learnt. He was glad that at last he had found something that he knew God wanted him to do. He wrote a hymn about it, which Sikhs still read today.

"I was like a singer with no one to sing for,
The Lord gave me a song to sing.
He said 'Night and day, sing my praise'.
I will sing your song, O Lord.
I will spread your word."

Wherever Nanak travelled, he sang God's praises. When people asked Nanak a question, he often replied with a song or a poem that helped them to understand and remember what he had taught them.

People also remembered Nanak's actions. At that time in India people would only sit to eat with those who had the same religion or the same position in society as themselves. Nanak taught them that all people are equal, and he showed this by inviting anyone who came to see him, rich or poor, Hindu or Muslim, to sit down to a meal together.

Nanak's followers called him Guru Nanak because he was a good teacher. Those who follow his teachings today are called Sikhs. In the Sikh temples around the world, his words are still read and sung, for the Sikhs learnt his poems and hymns and wrote them down.

Note:
This story can be told in conjunction with work on 'Who celebrates our birthday?' in the *Infant Teacher's Handbook*, page 48.

Nanak and the Holy Men

This is a story about the childhood of Guru Nanak, the founder of Sikhism.

Nanak was a kind and good son, but there were times when he puzzled his parents. One day his father gave Nanak some money and said to him, "Go to the nearest town, and spend this money as wisely as you can." He hoped that Nanak would use the money to earn more money.

So Nanak set off with his friend Bala. On the way they met some holy men who lived in the forest. Nanak stopped to talk to them.

"How do you live in the forest, with no homes, no clothes, and no money?" Nanak asked the holy men.

"We do not need homes or clothes", said the holy men. "We eat when God sends us food."

"How long is it since you had some food?" asked Nanak.

"It is four days", they said.

Nanak turned to his friend Bala. "What a good job we came this way", he said. "Now I can use my father's money really well."

"Nanak!" said Bala. "Remember what he told you about it. He said you must spend the money wisely!"

"I know", said Nanak. "Come on, let's go to the town quickly."

When he got to the town, Nanak spent all the money his father had given him on food. He bought rice, and flour, and sugar and butter. Then he and Bala carried it all back to the holy men in the forest.

"Here you are!" cried Nanak. "Eat all you want today, and there will be some left for another day. God has sent you food!"

The holy men thanked him with all their hearts, and thanked God for his kindness. But Bala was worried. "What will your father say?" he asked.

"What have we done?" asked Nanak.

"We!" said Bala. "I had nothing to do with this. I tried to stop you, but you wouldn't listen!"

When they got home, Nanak's father was very angry. "You have wasted the money I gave you to do business with!" he shouted.

"But father," said Nanak, "this was the very best business I could possibly do!"

But his father could not see that Nanak had used the money in the way that he thought would do the most good.

Flags and Needles

Guru Nanak spent much of his life travelling around from place to place, teaching people about God, and about how they should live their lives. One day he came to the house of a rich merchant called Duni Chand. On the day that Guru

Nanak arrived, Duni Chand was giving a great feast in memory of his father who had died the year before. It was the custom at that time for people to invite holy men to such feasts, in the hope that the food given to the holy men would give a blessing to the dead person in the next world.

When Guru Nanak arrived at the house, he saw a large number of flags outside. He asked Duni Chand, "What is the meaning of all these flags?"

"They are to show how rich I am", said Duni Chand. "Every flag represents a thousand rupees. Look how many flags there are! I am a very rich man!"

Guru Nanak thought that Duni Chand was showing off, but he said nothing. A little later he turned to Duni Chand and said, "Look after this needle for me. Take great care of it, for I shall ask for it back in the next world."

Duni Chand did not want to upset Guru Nanak, because he was a holy man. So he went to his wife and told her what he had said. "What shall I do?" he said.

"Go and give it back to the Guru," she said, "for no one can take anything with them into the next world."

That made Duni Chand think. If he could not take even a tiny needle into the next world, what good were all his thousands of rupees? He went back to Guru Nanak.

"I have been wrong", he said. "I thought my riches were important. But now I see that it is more important to feed poor people."

"Put food in the mouth of the poor," said Guru Nanak, "then you will have something to take with you to the next world."

From that time onwards, Duni Chand became a follower of Guru Nanak.

Note:
This story can be told in conjunction with work on 'Sharing money' in the *Junior Teacher's Handbook*, page 66.

Guru Nanak and the Robber

Guru Nanak spent most of his time travelling and teaching people he met about God. His friend Mardana went with him. Every evening Mardana sat down and played his rebeck (a musical instrument like a small guitar) while Guru Nanak sang hymns of praise to God. They went from place to place, and stayed with anyone who offered them shelter for the night.

Then one night they came to a place where a man called Sajjan lived. Sajjan was famous because he spent most of the day praying, and he always welcomed travellers to his house at night. Sajjan seemed to be a very kind person, but he was not. Every time someone stayed at his house, he killed them and stole their money and clothes.

When he saw Guru Nanak coming, he thought to himself, "This looks like someone with a lot of money." So he invited Guru Nanak and Mardana to stay the night. He gave them a good supper, and then said, "Here is your bedroom. I expect you are tired after your long journey, and you want to go to bed early?"

Guru Nanak and Mardana said "Thank you", and went into the room. But they did not go to sleep. Sajjan waited and waited for them to go to sleep so that he could kill them. But, as the night wore on, he could still hear voices and music. At last he went up to the door of the room, and listened to find out what was going on. It was then that he heard the most beautiful music. Guru Nanak and Mardana were singing and playing hymns and praising God. Sajjan listened and listened. And as he listened, something happened to him. The music and the beautiful words about God made him realise how bad he had been. He went into the room and fell at Guru Nanak's feet.

"I am a bad man!" he sobbed. "I have killed people and stolen their money! What shall I do?"

"Do not fear", said Guru Nanak. "If you are truly sorry for everything you have done, and if you decide not to do it any more, then God will forgive you."

"Oh, I am sorry, I am, I am!" cried Sajjan.

"Then you must give away everything that you have ever

stolen." said Guru Nanak. "Bring all the things here and give them to the poor."

And that is just what Sajjan did. He gave away all his money, and he turned his house into a place to worship God. He listened to everything that Guru Nanak had to say, and he began to tell other people about it.

Once again Sajjan became famous as a man who prayed a lot. But this time it was true.

⋖▢▷

Lehna and the Grass

Guru Nanak always taught people that doing hard or dirty work to help other people was important for anyone who wanted to be a good Sikh. One of his followers was a man called Lehna. Lehna was always willing to do any sort of work that needed doing.

One day Lehna came to visit Guru Nanak. He put on his best clothes and set off from the village where he lived. When he got near to Guru Nanak's village, some Sikhs were out in the fields gathering grass to take into the village for the cows to eat. Just as Lehna passed by, a large, wet bundle of muddy grass was ready to be carried to the village.

"I will take it", said Lehna, and picked up the bundle. He carried the heavy bundle on his head, and as he walked, the mud from the grass dripped down, all over his beautiful new clothes. But Lehna walked on, not at all upset.

Just then Guru Nanak's wife saw him. "Is this how Sikhs treat a good man?" she asked. "By making him carry the heaviest, dirtiest bundle?"

"You do not understand", said Guru Nanak. "That is not a load of grass, but a crown to honour the best of men!"

⋖▢▷

Guru Nanak Chooses a Successor

A time came when Guru Nanak knew that he was shortly to die. He did not want to leave the Sikhs alone. He wanted to leave another Guru to be their teacher and guide after him. But who should he choose? Some people thought that he would choose one of his two sons, but Guru Nanak believed that the Guru should not be chosen simply because he had been born into the right family. He believed that the Guru should be the person who was best able to help the Sikhs. The next Guru had to be someone who would obey and serve God and Guru Nanak humbly, without asking any questions.

One of Guru Nanak's followers was a man called Bhai Lehna. Bhai Lehna was a man who thought of God all the time. He loved to serve Guru Nanak and was always obedient to him. Guru Nanak had tested Bhai Lehna's obedience several times, and every time Bhai Lehna had shown that he was a true follower of the Guru.

Once Guru Nanak was holding a cup, but it slipped from his hand into a pit of dirty water. The Guru asked his sons to take it out of the pit. They refused to do so because they didn't want to get themselves dirty. But Bhai Lehna did not care about getting himself dirty. Straight away he went into the pit and got out the cup. He then washed it and gave it back to Guru Nanak. Another time, on a dark rainy night, a part of the Guru's house fell down. The Guru asked his sons to build up the wall again. They said that it was late and cold and dark, and anyway it wasn't their job to build walls. They said that the Guru should wait until morning and get a workman to mend the wall. Guru Nanak said that it wasn't a job for the workman. It was a job for the Sikhs to do, the followers of Guru Nanak. He did not have to ask Bhai Lehna. He just looked at him. Bhai Lehna at once got up and built up the wall. After a while the Guru looked at the wall, and said, "It's not straight. Take it down and build it up again."

At once Bhai Lehna obeyed. He took down the wall and built it again very carefully. The Guru still wasn't satisfied. He told Bhai Lehna to take the wall down again. Bhai Lehna took the wall down again and built it again very, very carefully. The Guru looked at the wall and said, "Ah, but it is not in the right place. It should have been built here and not there." Bhai Lehna did not ask the Guru any questions. He took the wall down and built it again where the Guru had told him, but the Guru was still not satisfied. He told Bhai Lehna to take the wall down and build it up again. So again Bhai Lehna obeyed without asking any questions. Eventually one of the Guru's sons said to Bhai Lehna, "He will never be satisfied, give it up". But Bhai Lehna pointed out that he was just the servant of the Guru. It isn't for the servant to decide what the work should be. The master decides and the servant just does the work.

Everyday Guru Nanak used to get up three hours before dawn and bathe in the river. Bhai Lehna always went with him to look after his clothes. One day, three other Sikhs decided to go with Bhai Lehna and also look after the Guru's clothes. They saw that the Guru was pleased with Bhai Lehna and they wanted to please him too, but it was a cold winter's day. Soon the wind began to blow and hail began to form. The other three Sikhs could not bear to sit and guard the Guru's clothes any longer. It was too cold for them. So they went back. When the Guru came out of the river, he said to Bhai Lehna, "The others went, why didn't you go too?" Bhai Lehna replied, "A servant shouldn't leave his master. You were here, how could I go?"

Bhai Lehna showed his obedience to Guru Nanak in many other ways too. Guru Nanak loved him so much that he called him Angad, which means 'part of myself'. Because Angad had been so obedient to Guru Nanak, the Guru knew that this was the best person to become the leader and teacher of the Sikhs after him.

Note:
This story can be told in conjunction with work on 'Choosing a successor', in the *Junior Teacher's Handbook*, page 102.

Bhai Ghanaiya

I n the time of Guru Gobind Singh, Sikhs often had to fight for their beliefs. Once, when they were fighting against the Turks, some Sikhs came to the Guru at the end of one day's fighting and accused a Sikh named Ghanaiya of helping the Turks.

They said that Ghanaiya was going about the battlefield, giving water and other kinds of help to the Turks who had been wounded in the battle. This made the Turks well enough to fight the Sikhs again. They said that Guru Gobind Singh should tell Bhai Ghanaiya to stop helping the Turks.

When he heard about this, the Guru sent for Bhai Ghanaiya. Bhai Ghanaiya came to the Guru, who asked him, "Ghanaiya, I hear that you have been helping our enemies. Is this true?"

Ghanaiya replied, "No, I have never given any help to an enemy."

The Sikhs told the Guru that Bhai Ghaniya was lying. "We haven't made a mistake; we saw him with our own eyes giving water to the enemies."

The Guru said to Bhai Ghanaiya, "I know you very well. I know you don't lie, but my Sikhs don't lie either. Tell me the truth about what happened."

Bhai Ghanaiya answered, "It's true that I have been giving water and help to the Turks as well as to the Sikhs, but I wasn't serving any Turk or Sikh. I was serving you my Guru."

Guru Gobind Singh said, "Go on, explain. How were you serving me?"

"Well," said Bhai Ghaniya, "you have told us that if we feed the hungry, we are feeding you; that if we clothe the naked, we are clothing you. As I have been walking through these wounded soldiers, I did not see Sikhs or Turks. All I saw was my Guru. I saw the true Guru, God, in every one of them."

"Well done, Ghanaiya, you have done the right thing", said the Guru. "While we are fighting against the Turks, they are our enemies, but when they need our help, they are our fellow human beings and we must help them." The Guru then gave Bhai Ghanaiya ointment to help him with his work, and told him to carry on giving help to the wounded.

3/98

The Khalsa

Many years ago, in India, wicked men tried to stop Sikhs praying to God in their own way. It got so bad that Sikhs started to fear for their lives. Nevertheless they still gathered in a small town called Anandpur to celebrate their harvest festival. They sang and danced and watched horse races, and they said "Thank you" to God for the harvest. During the festival, Guru Gobind was sitting outside his tent. Suddenly he stood up and called for silence.

"All Sikhs listen to me", he cried. "We must be brave, we must not let our enemies frighten us. Loving God and obeying him must be the most important things in our lives; more important than money and houses; more important than even our families and our friends. We must be willing to give up everything in order to serve God, even our lives."

All the people cheered. Then Guru Gobind called them again.

"Are you willing to give up your lives for God? Is there one of you who would come forward and die for God?"

There was silence. Many people looked very frightened. Then one man came and stood before the Guru. His name was Dayaram. "I am willing to die for God", he said.

So Guru Gobind and Dayaram went into the tent. After a little while the Guru came out alone. In his hand was a sword dripping with blood. The people looked at each other. What could have happened?

"Is there a second man", asked Guru Gobind, "who is willing to die for God?"

Another man stepped forward and disappeared into the tent. A third, a fourth and a fifth man volunteered. Each one entered the tent, and each time the Guru appeared again with his sword dripping with blood. The crowd waited quietly. How brave these men had been! They had died for love of God.

Suddenly the Guru pulled back the flaps of the tent. There stood the five men, dressed in yellow robes, wearing turbans and carrying long swords.

"From now on these men shall be called the five loved ones", said Guru Gobind, "because they love God so much and God loves them."

Then Gobind and his wife baptised the five loved ones with sweet water called amrit. They in turn baptised the Guru and his family. Now the people were no longer afraid. They all came forward and were baptised with amrit.

"In future", said Guru Gobind, "every Sikh man will add the name Singh, which means lion, to his name. And every Sikh woman will add the name Kaur, which means princess, to her name. And now that we are brave," said Guru Gobind Singh, "we want every one to know that we are Sikhs. We will never cut our hair. We will keep it tidy with a comb called a kanga. We will wear an iron bracelet called a kara. We will carry a small sword – a kirpan – and the men will wear turbans. And we will always wear clothes suitable for horse-riding – kacchera – so that we are ready to ride into battle to defend our faith."

Note:
This story can be told in conjunction with work in the *Junior Assembly Book* on 'Baisakhi – against injustice', page 10, and on 'Submitting voluntarily to law', page 62. Further information on the Khalsa can be found in the *Infant Teacher's Handbook*, page 96 and in the *Junior Teacher's Handbook*, page 131.

Tales of Money and Other Riches

King Midas

A story from Ancient Rome

King Midas loved gold. He liked the way it sparkled in the sun. He liked to feel its weight. He liked its yellowness. All his subjects knew the way to please him most was to offer him gifts of gold – coins, chalices, jewellery – he loved them all.

Now one day the king was walking in his palace grounds when he came across an old satyr slumped at the foot of a tree. Midas recognized him at once as Silenus, follower and friend of the god of wine and pleasure, Dionysus. He also saw that Silenus was drunk.

"Come on, old thing", he said, helping the satyr on to his hooves (satyrs are half goat and half man). "Let's return you to your master. I think I know where he is just now."

Dionysus was much relieved to see his friend safe and well, if a bit the worse for drink, and he thanked Midas profusely. "What gift can I give you to show my thanks?" he said. "Ask and I will make it possible."

Midas didn't have to think – he knew at once what he wanted.

He had often lain awake and wondered what he would wish for if such a chance came. "Turn everything I touch into gold!" he replied. "That is what I want. That is my heart's desire."

Dionysus looked at him sorrowfully. "Are you sure? That is a wish filled with danger. Much harm could come of it."

But Midas was certain, and would not change his mind. So, reluctantly, Dionysus granted the wish.

Midas began the walk back to the palace. He couldn't wait to get there to try out his new gift. But why wait? He reached out and broke a twig from a nearby tree. To his delight it was at once transformed from dull brown bark to shiny, heavy, yellow gold. He picked up pebbles from the road, those too turned into gold. He touched one tree, two, three, four trees until soon he was walking through a golden avenue, beautiful but oh so still – for gold is dead and cold.

On his return to his palace, Midas set about making his home "equal to the home of the gods". He ran about like an excited child touching everything in sight – the tables, the chairs, the reclining couch. Everything turned to gold at Midas' touch. The vases filled with fresh spring flowers, the lizard lying lazily on a stone slab, the bird singing in its cage – all changed instantly into the shining yellow metal that Midas loved so much.

As he continued, the servants, who had watched in wonder, began to creep away – fearful at the sight of so much cold metal, and of the sudden silence that had descended on the room. Nothing moved but the king, who leapt and sang and danced about the room rejoicing in his good fortune. He was wealthy beyond his dreams, but more than that he was surrounded by what he loved the best – gold. He could sit in his room and take pleasure in it, day after day.

But soon the excitement began to make him hungry and thirsty. He sat on his chair, a bit uncomfortable now it was gold, and called for food and drink. A bowl of fruit was brought to him, and Midas picked out a ripe peach, looking forward to its sweet juiciness. Instead his teeth jarred on the hard gold it had become. He tried to drink from the golden chalice but the wine turned to liquid gold as it touched his lips.

Slowly the truth dawned on him. If everything he touched turned to gold then he could no longer eat or drink. He would never find a resting place, for every bed and cushion would be solid gold. How would he live? Now he hated the very thing he had most longed for.

But worse was to come. As he sat there head in hands his young daughter came running into the room her arms flung wide to embrace her father.

"No!" screamed Midas – but it was too late. She had touched him. The laughing child, so full of life, was turned into a lifeless statue.

"O Father Dionysus!" cried out Midas in anguish and pain. "Have pity on me. Forgive me my terrible mistake, and take from me this gift which curses me."

And Dionysus had pity on Midas and forgave him his foolishness, and took from him the golden touch.

Note:
This story can be told in conjunction with work on 'Money' in the *Junior Teacher's Handbook*, page 64.

Justice and Mercy

A Jewish story

In a tiny cottage, near the gates of a great city, lived a poor tailor called Reuben, his wife and his four children. The people in the city were rich and bought their fine clothes from merchants. Few came to Reuben to have their clothes made for them.

One day Reuben's wife became ill and needed expensive medicines to make her well again. Reuben went to the house of a rich merchant and begged for money, promising that he would pay back the loan in fourteen days. The merchant was not an unkind man, and he gave Reuben what he needed.

The fourteen days passed, then fifteen, then sixteen, but Reuben did not return to pay his debt. He had worked hard in the shop, but had not made enough money to repay the money he owed. At last the merchant came to his humble shop.

"Are you able to repay me?" he asked.

"No master", replied Reuben.

"Then we must go to the Judge. He will decide what must be done."

So they walked to the city gates where the Judge sat each day. When his turn came the merchant explained to the Judge what had happened. When the Judge had heard what the merchant had to say he asked Reuben, "Have you anything to say for yourself?"

"What the merchant says is true", Reuben replied. "I have worked every day and every night but I have not been able to earn enough money to repay the loan."

Many of the spectators whispered angrily among themselves. "The merchant is rich. He wouldn't miss the money. Why doesn't he cancel the loan? Why doesn't he give Reuben the money as a gift in gratitude for the all the wealth he has amassed while Reuben and his family have lived in poverty?"

The judge called for silence. "Justice requires that the money be repaid," he said.

The people began to mutter angrily, and Reuben hung his head in despair. Then to everyone's amazement the Judge left the judgement seat and came to stand among the people. He took off his judge's hat and held it upside down.

"Now, all of you who grieve for Reuben put your hands into your pockets and give what you can to help him repay the money he owes – for that is mercy, and that is what justice requires."

The King Who Was Greedy

A Jewish story

L ong ago, there lived a king who was very, very, greedy. He had so many treasures that he kept a host of slaves just to build new storehouses to keep them in. But he was never satisfied. Every year he demanded more and more taxes from his subjects: gold, silver and precious jewels. And, when the people had no more money to give him, he took their wheat and barley; their oranges and lemons; their cattle and their sheep.

One day there came a time when the sun shone every day and there was no rain. The ground grew dry and parched. The streams dried up. The crops failed. The animals died. The people told the King's messengers that they had hardly anything left to live on for the coming year. But it was no use. The king demanded payment or their houses and farms would be seized and their children sold into slavery.

In the town lived an old man, much loved for his gentleness and learning.

"I will go to the king", he said. "I am too old to be afraid that he might kill me."

So he went to the palace walls called to the king. "Your Majesty, your people are starving and dying from thirst. Their crops and their animals have died. You have taken all they have in taxes but what do you give them in return? Nothing! If they all die where will your kingdom be? You must help them if you wish to have a people over whom you can rule."

The king was angry. "How dare you question my actions! Now I will demand even more taxes."

But the old man showed no fear. "Your Majesty, I am a fisherman. All my life I have fished on your beautiful lake, but soon my life will be over for I am old. Grant me one small favour. Sail with me in my boat so that all the people may know that I am the king's friend."

The king meant to refuse, but it was a beautiful day. Perhaps it would be pleasant to sail on the lake. He ordered the palace gates to be opened, and together king and subject went down to the water's edge. Soon the boat reached the middle of the lake. The old man took up a drill and began to drill a hole through the bottom of the boat under his seat. The boat began to fill with water.

"What are you doing?" asked the King. "We shall drown!"

"Do not worry sire," the fisherman replied, "I am boring the hole under my seat, not yours. You have nothing to fear."

At first the King was speechless with terror but gradually understanding dawned upon his face.

"Put down the drill. Let us fill up the hole with rags and let us row for the shore. You are a wise teacher. I understand what you are trying to tell me. We share in each other's fate in the boat. We share in each other's fate in my kingdom. My greed has bored a hole in my kingdom. It is under my subjects' lands and homes, but

I too will suffer. Let us return so that I may fill up the hole in my kingdom before it is destroyed."

The Best Merchandise

10/98

A Jewish story

A merchant ship was ready to sail to a far away country. It was filled with gold and silver, with spices and rich silks and satins, jewellery and exotic fruits. Just before the gangplank was raised, a scholar joined the passengers, carrying only one small bag for his personal needs.

"What kind of merchandise do you sell?" they asked.

"The best", he replied.

The ship set sail. As the days passed the merchants grew more and more puzzled, and they searched the ship to see what the scholar had to sell. But they found nothing.

"He must be a madman", they said, and decided to ignore him.

But when they reached the middle of the ocean a great storm arose. The ship was driven onto a deserted shore and wrecked on the sharp rocks. Passengers and sailors all swam to safety but the cargo was lost. With nothing but the clothes they were wearing, they set off overland. Eventually, they came to the city where they had hoped to sell their goods. The merchants had to seek for generous people who would give them food and shelter.

The scholar, however, went to the Synagogue and began to teach the students there. Immediately they recognised that he was a wonderful teacher. They offered him hospitality and begged him to stay and teach them every day.

After many weeks a ship came to take all the shipwrecked merchants home. When the students and members of the Synagogue came to say goodbye to their teacher, they brought him rich gifts in gratitude for all he had taught them. But all the merchants walked sadly along the beach. They still had nothing but the clothes they were wearing. They could not pay the necessary fare. Generously the teacher paid for their passage.

"You were right, Rabbi", they said. "Yours really is the best merchandise."

<hr />

Ali's Hajj

In 632 CE, just before he died, Muhammad, the great prophet of the Muslim people, made a pilgrimage to Makkah. He told his followers that God wanted all Muslims to make this journey once in their lives. This would show that they were willing to give up time, money and pleasures in order to obey God, and show him how much they loved him. It costs lots of money to make the journey, and some Muslims save up all their lives so that they can afford to go to Makkah. They say they are going on 'Hajj', which means to set out on a journey. This is one of the stories about Hajj that Muslims like to tell.

Many years ago, there lived a Muslim called Ali who made a living by mending sandals and shoes. For thirty years he had been saving up all the money he made from his business so that he could go on Hajj. At last he had enough! He made sure that his family had plenty of money and food so that they would be well looked after while he was away, and a friend promised him that he would mind his shop. The great day came. His friends were waiting for him. They too were going to Makkah.

"Just a moment," he said, "I must go and say good-bye to my neighbour." He went to the house next door and knocked.

"Come in."

"I have come to say good-bye", said Ali.

The family were eating their morning meal. "That stew smells good", said Ali. "Can I have a little before I set out on my journey?"

His neighbours looked very sad. "We cannot offer any of our food", they said. Ali was surprised and hurt. Then his neighbours explained: "We haven't eaten for seven days. This morning, we found a dead chicken. It hadn't been killed in the correct Muslim way, but we know that God will not be angry if we eat this meat rather than go hungry for another day. But it would be wrong for you to eat it – a good Muslim does not eat such meat."

Ali stood very quietly. He was thinking hard. How could he spend so much money to go on Hajj when his neighbours had not eaten for seven days? He felt ashamed.

"Here," he said, "take this money and feed your children."

He thought to himself, "This will be my Hajj." He gave his neighbours the money that he had saved for Hajj, and went back to his home.

Back at home his friends were waiting for him. "Hurry up", they said. "We have a long way to travel today."

"I have few things to do", said Ali. "You go on, I'll catch you up later."

But of course he didn't. Many weeks later, his friends returned. A little sadly Ali asked them, "Did you enjoy the Hajj?"

"Of course, we did", they replied. "But you know that. We saw you there."

Did they really see him there? Ali knew that they were mistaken, but he saw it as a sign from Allah that his gift would count as his pilgrimage.

Baucis and Philemon

A story from Ancient Greece

There came a time, long, long ago, when the gods decided to travel to the earth. Zeus, the king of the gods, and Hermes, his messenger, came from their heavenly home on Mount Olympus. They made themselves look like ordinary men. They came to a place where there were good farms and fine houses, and the people clearly had plenty to eat and plenty of wine to drink. The gods thought that in a place where there was such plenty they would easily find someone to give them a meal and a bed for the night. So they went round, knocking on doors, asking for a simple meal and a place to sleep. But no one would give them so much as a crust of bread and a cup of water! They knocked on a hundred doors, but no one gave them anything.

At last they left the village, and walked towards a very small, poor-looking hut a little way away. In this hut lived an old man called Philemon, and an old woman called Baucis. They had been married since they were quite young, and had always lived together happy and contented, although they were very poor. They saw the two strangers coming, and they did not wait to be asked. They ran out and invited them into the hut, to have supper and spend the night. Baucis and Philemon did not have anything ready to give the strangers to eat, but they hurried round and began to prepare a meal. Philemon fetched vegetables from the garden, and Baucis began to cook them, fetching a small piece of bacon to flavour the stew. And as they worked, they made their guests sit down by the fire, and chatted with them to make them feel welcome and at home.

At last the meal was ready, and Baucis began to lay the table. They only had two rough wooden chairs, but Baucis covered them with some cloths she had woven herself. The table was old and did not stand steady, so Philemon fetched a tile to put under one of the legs to make it steadier. There was no fine china or glass, but Baucis fetched their best clay bowls for the stew, and Philemon brought two wooden cups for the wine.

Then they served the meal to their guests. There were olives and hard bread, and the vegetable stew, and fruit and honey-comb, and one small clay jug of wine – all they had. The two gods sat down to this simple meal, and ate hungrily, and drank the wine eagerly. But after a while, Philemon and Baucis noticed a strange thing. Philemon kept pouring the wine, but no matter how much the strangers drank, there was always plenty more in the jug!

Then Philemon and Baucis realised that their guests must be gods in disguise. In terror they knelt down before Zeus and Hermes.

"Please forgive us", they said. "The meal we have given you is not worthy of gods, and we have given it to you on clay plates, with only old chairs to sit on. What can we give you that is a proper sacrifice for the gods?"

They decided that in honour of the gods, they must kill their only goose, which lived outside the hut, and kept guard for them. So they went out to catch the goose and kill it for a sacrifice for the gods. But they could not catch the goose! Round and round it ran, with Baucis and Philemon chasing it. At last, the goose ran in the hut, and hid behind the two gods. Baucis and Philemon followed, out of breath.

"Do not fear", said Zeus. "We did not come for sacrifices. We came to see if people on earth will welcome strangers and give them food. Your neighbours gave us nothing, but you have given us the best you had. They will have what they deserve, and so will you. Follow me."

So Baucis and Philemon followed the gods out of their hut and up the steep hillside. When they got to the top, Zeus said, "Look down."

They looked, and saw that where the village had been, there was nothing but a huge lake. On the shores of this lake stood their old hut. But as they watched, they saw it changing. Their old and shabby hut turned into a beautiful temple to the gods.

"Now", said Zeus, "you can ask anything you like of me as a reward for making us welcome."

The old couple looked at each other for a moment and then told Zeus what they wanted.

"Please, we would like to live in the temple and take care of it for the gods. And because we have loved each other all our lives, we would like to die at the same moment, so that one of us is not left to mourn the other."

"Your wish is granted," said Zeus, and left them.

So Baucis and Philemon lived happily in the temple, taking care of it for the gods. And when they were both very old, they stood outside the door together, arm in arm, gazing at the lake. As they stood there, they were changed. At exactly the same moment, Baucis and Philemon changed into two trees, their branches entwined together.

And people say that you can still see those two trees today, standing by the lake.

Note:
This story can be told in conjunction with work on 'Sharing food' in the *Junior Teacher's Handbook*, page 34.

The Soupstone

A long while ago, in a cold country, a traveller was walking along a forest path. He was tired and hungry, and in his pack he had nothing to eat. He came to a a village, and wondered if they would give him anything to eat. Would the villagers even have anything much to eat themselves?

Suddenly he had an idea. He picked up a large stone from the side of the road, put it in his pack, and trudged on to the village.

When he arrived, he did not ask for food. He asked instead for a large cooking pot, some water, and a fire to heat it on.

"In return", he said, "I will share my soup with you all."

"Soup?" said the villagers. "What soup?"

"The most delicious soup you have ever tasted", said the traveller. "Made with this magic stone that I carry with me. But don't take my word for it – wait and taste it."

So they gave him the pot full of water, and he put his stone in the bottom and put it on the fire. As it began to simmer, he stirred it round and said: "Mmm – my mouth's beginning to water already! By the way, I don't suppose anyone has an onion? It's not necessary, but it would make the soup even better. Or maybe a carrot, or a turnip, or a small potato?"

So the villagers went to their houses, and one or two brought onions and potatoes, one a carrot, another a turnip, and the traveller cut them up and put them in the soup. He stirred it and let it simmer it for a while longer, and a delicious smell began to come from the pot.

"I'll tell you what would really bring out the full flavour of this magic soup. If anyone has a little piece of chicken, it would make it extra special. It's delicious already, but it would just add that little something."

So one or two of the villagers brought small pieces of chicken that they had been saving for their own family's supper, and put them in the soup.

Once again the traveller stirred the soup and simmered it, and by this time everyone's mouth was watering at the delicious smell that came from the pot.

"Nearly ready now", he said. "But just as a final finishing touch, can someone find a tiny bit of parsley, and some salt and pepper?"

One villager picked a sprig of parsley from her garden, others brought salt and pepper, and the soup simmered for just a few more minutes.

"Now it's ready!" he said. "Bring bowls and spoons – don't forget one for me – and I will share it out."

So the whole village, and the traveller, ate their fill of the magic soup. And it was even more delicious than the traveller had said.

Note:
This story can be told in conjunction with work on 'Sharing food', in the *Junior Teacher's Handbook*, page 34.

The Story of Baboushka

A Russian story

Baboushka's house was the cleanest and neatest in the whole village; some said it was the cleanest and neatest in the whole of Russia. From morning to night she swept and washed, polished and cleaned. No speck of dirt was ever allowed to remain in her little cottage. No spider had ever made a home in a corner of her room. No ant or mouse had ever found a crumb or scrap to make their meal. The windows gleamed and sparkled in the sun, and people said that the front step was so well scrubbed that you could eat from it.

Early one evening Baboushka was busy about her kitchen as usual. The rich warm smell of baking bread filled the little room, and a pot of thick soup bubbled on the stove. Suddenly there was a knock on the door.

"I'm coming, I'm coming!" called Baboushka, wiping her hands on her apron and straightening her hair, as she went to see who could be calling on her so unexpectedly.

It was her neighbour. "Come quickly, Baboushka, and see a most wonderful sight. There's a new star in the sky. It shines so bright and beautiful. You must look."

"But I have bread in the oven and soup on the stove, my pots are not yet scrubbed. I cannot come", replied Baboushka.

"This will take but a minute. Your bread will not burn, and your soup will not stick, and the pots, well surely the pots can wait a few moments until they are clean again? Do come, Baboushka", pleaded her neighbour.

But Baboushka refused. "I'll come when I am ready, and not before", she said and shut the door.

All through the evening there were knocks on the door and friends and neighbours urging her to come and look at the star, but all through the evening Baboushka always had just one more job to do and would not come.

Then came a final knock. "Not another!" grumbled Baboushka as she flung wide the door. "Can't a person be left in peace to do her ...". She stopped open-mouthed in mid-sentence, for there on the door step were three men the like of which she had never seen before. They were dressed in fine clothes and were clearly men of wealth and importance.

"Foreigners", thought Baboushka – for no Russian had skin as black as one and golden brown as the other. "Foreigners and kings for sure".

Then one of them spoke, "Kind woman, we three are travellers, worn and weary from the journey. We seek a warm bed for the night and a hot supper."

"But... but my house is too humble for men as great as you", stuttered Baboushka. "The blankets are too rough, my food too simple."

"Your house is clean, the smell of your bread and soup is enticing. It is good enough for us", was the response.

And so it was that Baboushka gave hospitality that night to three kings. She wanted to wait on them while they sat at her table, but they would not have it, and made her sit and eat with them. It was a happy meal. Baboushka listened with ever-increasing wonder as they told her of their adventures on their travels – but most of all the reason for their journey. They were following the star – the very star her neighbours had beckoned her to see – for they believed it would take them to the birthplace of a new king, a prince truly sent from God, the promised Christchild.

"Just imagine, Baboushka, a king sent from God, a prince of peace and love", they said. "Baboushka, why don't you come with us, why don't you come and give honour to the Christchild?"

For one brief moment Baboushka nearly said "Yes" but then she remembered all the things that needed doing. The sheets on the beds where the kings had slept – they would need washing, drying and ironing. The stove wanted cleaning. She had noticed a small tear in a table-cloth. It must be mended, and she would need to save up to buy a present fit for a king.

"No, I cannot come", she said. "Perhaps later."

Next morning the kings asked her again: "Would she come with them?", but Baboushka would not.

When the kings had left Baboushka set about her tasks that day without her usual vigour and enthusiasm. She couldn't help thinking about the three kings and their quest to find the Christchild, and she thought too of her own baby who had died many years ago while still a child. She still had his clothes and toys stored safely in her painted wooden chest. She thought too of the gifts the kings were taking. Gold, frankincense and myrrh. What sort of gifts were those for a baby? Could he play with them? Would they make him chortle and laugh? No, they would not!

Then Baboushka did something very unusual for her. She stopped what she was doing – right in the middle without finishing it. She left the duster on the mantelpiece and went to find her treasures. She opened the painted wooden chest and one by one took out the toys, the toys she had not seen for so long. Here was the wicker rattle that her baby had waved round and round. She remembered his smiling and laughing as he thwacked himself on the head with it. Here was the little wooden horse on wheels that his grandad had made him. Here was the cloth ball she had stitched for him.

"Another baby could have joy from these toys", Baboushka thought to herself. "Even a king would love a wooden horse like this."

For the rest of that day, and long into the night, Baboushka washed, mended and polished these toys and others until they looked like new. Then she took each one, wrapped it tenderly in cloth and packed it in her basket.

Next day she pulled on her embroidered sheepskin jacket, tied her woollen scarf under her chin, tucked the basket full of toys under her arm and set off on her journey.

"Where are you going, Baboushka?" asked the villagers when they saw her leave.

"I am going to find the prince of peace, the Christchild", she replied. "I want to follow the kings. Which way did they go, for I cannot see the star of which they spoke."

"They went west", was the answer. "Go that way Baboushka. Hurry and you might catch them."

But Baboushka did not catch up with her noble visitors. She asked at every town and village she came to, and at every town and village she heard the same, "Yes, three men dressed in great finery had passed through, but they had since traveled on". And she was pointed in their direction.

The days turned into weeks, and the weeks into months, but Baboushka walked on, eager in her desire to see the Christchild, eager to give him the gifts she carried. On the way she travelled through mountains and valleys and lands such as she had never imagined, with strange languages, strange food and costumes.

Sometimes she slept out in the open sheltered only by a haystack, sometimes she curled up in the barns, and sometimes kind folk gave her refuge in their homes.

Once, passing an open window, she caught a glimpse of a baby gurgling in its cot. She stood and watched it, charmed by its innocence. She looked around and saw the poverty of the child's home...not many toys here. With sudden impulse she took a toy from her basket and popped it in the child's crib. The Christchild would not miss one toy, surely not?

Again and again Baboushka left toys with children on her journey – always secretly through open door and window, and on the way she found discarded toys and mended them to fill her basket.

Eventually, footsore and weary she reached the land of Israel. Was this at last the place? She wondered in what great palace she would find the baby king. Herod's palace perhaps – grand on the hill.

"Is there a new baby king in the palace?" she asked of a guard.

"Funny that," he said, "three fine gentlemen were making the same enquiry a few days ago, but no babe's been born here for a long time."

"Oh which way did they go – did you see?"

"No...I but I heard tell they went off in the direction of Bethlehem."

Baboushka picked up her basket once more, and trudged off along the dusty road south to Bethlehem. Would this road lead to the end of her journey?

On the hills outside Bethlehem she met a shepherd driving his sheep down into the town.

"You're a stranger in these parts", he said gazing at her costume.

"Many's a stranger we've had these days, and strange sights too. What brings you here?"

"I'm seeking the Christchild, prince of peace", she said.

"Why!" exclaimed the shepherd, "I have seen the Christchild, prince of peace. Born in stable over there he was. And I worshipped him – knelt at his feet I did. And there were three grand-looking men there too – kings they were, or wise men. They brought him gifts such as I have never seen before. Not much good for a baby though – gold, frankincense and myrrh. Come from the east they say."

Baboushka's heart leapt with joy. At last her journey was over! At last she would see the Christchild.

But it was not to be. When she arrived at the stable the little family, mother father and child, were not there. Instead, all she saw were an ass and an ox, which gazed forlornly at the vacant crib where once had lain the prince of peace.

"They went in the night." The innkeeper told her. "I came in the morning and they were gone."

What happened next? Some say Baboushka made her bed there that night, with ox and ass to watch over her, as they had watched over the Christchild. And as she lay there she wept in disappointment. "Oh Lord," she wept, "I have so longed to see you and to give you my gifts, and I am so so tired." And in her dreams she heard a voice: "Baboushka, Baboushka, you have seen me...You have met me on the way – every time you gave a gift it was as though you gave it to me. Come be with me now in Paradise."

When the innkeeper visited the stable next morning he found the old woman lying dead, but on her face was a smile of peaceful content.

Others say though that Baboushka continued on her search and still wanders the world today looking for the Christchild. And as she goes she still leaves toys for children in open windows and doors.

In Russia the children are sure this is true, for at Christmas they wake to find toys by their bed and they shout, "Baboushka has been, Baboushka has been!"

Note:
This story can be told in conjunction with work on 'In pursuit of true happiness' in the *Junior Assembly Book*, page 58.

Papa Panov

A Russian story

The cobbler Panov lived alone in a small room behind his little shop. Every day he sat by the window stitching at leather, or hammering at the soles of shoes. Sometimes he made a brand new pair, but more often than not he was mending the well-worn boots of the villagers – for this was a poor place and new shoes were a luxury.

In his youth he had been known as cobbler Panov, but now grown old and much loved for his kindness, he was called Papa Panov by friend and neighbour. He was like a papa, a father, to the whole village.

It was Christmas Eve. Ever since his wife had died and his children had gone to live in distant places, Papa Panov liked to spend the holy night reading again from the scriptures the story of the birth of the Christchild. This night, as he pictured Mary and Joseph being turned away from inn after inn, he wished that he could have been there to offer them his home. He wished that the Christchild had been his guest. While he thought and thought of it, it seemed to him that he heard a voice calling, "Papa Panov, Papa Panov, tomorrow I will come to your home. Tomorrow your wish will be fulfilled for I will visit you."

Papa Panov knew at once that it must be Jesus, the Christ, who had spoken to him. He jumped to his feet. If Jesus was visiting he must be ready for him! He had a thick soup on the stove, and bread freshly baked that very day. In the corner of the shop he had a piece of soft supple leather, a scrap left over from a pair of fine shoes he had once made for a wealthy lady. It was perfect for a pair of baby's shoes, perfect for a gift for the Christchild.

All night long he cut and sewed the little shoes with tiny, delicate stitches. When at last he had finished he couldn't help admiring his own workmanship – surely a king's son had never worn better? He put them carefully aside, lit the match under the saucepan to warm the soup, and opened the shutters. The pale winter sun was just rising over the rooftops.

Suddenly Papa Panov was overcome with anxiety. What time would Jesus come? And how would he recognize him? What age would he be? Would he come as a baby, or as a man? Would those shoes even fit him? He must watch carefully all day, never leaving his look-out by the window, until he could open the door to welcome Jesus as a guest.

Papa Panov looked up and down the street. A figure appeared around the corner. Was this him? Was this Jesus? No, it was only old Peter the road-sweeper shuffling his way through the slush, his threadbare coat flapping in the wind. Papa Panov felt a surge of irritation. What was he doing there littering up the place, making it a mess – unfit for his important visitor?

"Go faster, Peter, pass quickly!" Papa Panov silently willed. But how cold Peter looked, and hungry too!

Papa Panov hurried out into the street and took the road-sweeper by the arm.

"Peter, come in and warm yourself by my fire, and have some soup – tea too – but be quick. I am watching for someone very important."

He settled the old man by the stove and returned to his post, fearful that Jesus might have gone by without him noticing.

A short time later he heard a clatter and a banging. It was the tinker dragging his wares in his battered cart.

"I'm off home then", he called. "Been on the road a week, only another five miles to go."

Papa Panov had a brief argument with himself. Should he invite the tinker inside? He had an important visitor coming that day, much more important than the tinker. How could he entertain them both? On the other hand the tinker did look so very tired, and it was another two hour walk until the tinker would reach his own village.

"Come back, come back", he shouted out to the tinker. "Have some tea, and some soup to warm you on your way. There's a bit of bread as well."

When the tinker and the road-sweeper had both eaten well they moved on, leaving Papa Panov still standing by the window watching. Which way would Jesus come? If only he knew! Suddenly a young woman came into view. She carried a small child on her hip and a rough bundle of clothes was flung over her shoulder. She and the child looked blue with the cold. This time there was no hesitation. Papa Panov beckoned them into his home, and offered them soup which they accepted gladly.

"The landlord told us we must leave", the young woman explained. "I'm going on to my sister's. I think she'll take us."

Papa Panov looked at the child. "Her clothes are so thin", he thought. "How can they protect her against the icy wind?" So he fetched a blanket from the bed and tore it in half. "Here, have this", he said, wrapping it round the child. "That will help keep out the cold. The other half will make a shawl for your mother." Then he noticed that the child's feet were bare. "No shoes, no wonder the mother was carrying her!" he said to himself.

He looked at the tiny shoes he had stitched so lovingly, lying on the shelf ready for the Christchild. He looked at the child's feet again. Yes, they would fit, and she had need of them. Sadly he picked them up and stroked them, sorry because he had wanted them especially for the Christchild. Nevertheless he slipped them gently onto his small guest's feet. "There, that's better", he muttered.

Throughout that day people came and went from Papa Panov's little shop. Travellers who had lost their way, poor folk looking for work, children playing outside to keep from under their mothers' feet. Papa Panov welcomed them all.

Dusk fell Papa Panov took one last look up and down the street before he closed the shutters. As he turned from the window and went to get ready for the night he wiped a tear from his eye. His disappointment was great. He had wanted so much to see the Christchild. He lit the candles in front of his picture of Mary with the baby Jesus, and sank wearily into his big armchair.

"Oh, Lord," he cried out, "why did you not come? I so longed for you."

It seemed that a voice spoke in reply: "But I did come, Papa Panov. Did you not see me? I was the road-sweeper you fed. I was the tinker you gave a drink to. I was the child you clothed. Remember the words of the scriptures. I was hungry and you fed me. I was thirsty and you took me in. I was naked and you clothed me. When you welcomed all those people today, Papa Panov, you welcomed me."

Then Papa Panov knew that his wish had been fulfilled. He had welcomed the Christchild that day after all.

Tales of the Wise and the Foolish

A Man, a Boy and a Donkey

A traditional European story

Down the road walked an old man and his young grand-son. Beside them trotted a donkey. They were all very happy, for the sun shone brightly and the breeze carried the smell of orange blossom. Another traveller passed them going in the opposite direction. He stopped and stared and shouted: "Why are you walking? Don't you know that donkeys are made for riding?"

After a little thought, the boy and his grandfather decided that what the stranger said was good advice, so they climbed on to the donkey's back. As they approached the city passers by began to point at them, and to mutter angrily to each other. Eventually, one man ran forward and caught hold of the donkey's bridle.

"Aren't you ashamed of yourselves – two of you riding on such a small donkey? How can you be so cruel?"

The boy looked at his grandfather. Of course, how could they have been so thoughtless! He jumped down, took the bridle and led the donkey towards the city gates. Soon they passed a water carrier. He looked angrily at the grandfather.

"How can you let a young boy walk whilst you ride – and don't you think you're too heavy for that small donkey?"

The old man shook his head in bewilderment. "Perhaps the water carrier was right. Help me down, Grandson. Now you must ride."

Eventually they reached the middle of the city. Outside an inn the innkeeper was serving some merchants with wine.

"Just imagine a strong boy like you letting your old grandfather walk while you ride comfortably. Have you no respect for your elders? You're a disgrace!"

So a little further on the three stopped, and the boy slipped from the donkey's back. What were they to do? People grumbled if they both rode the donkey, if neither rode the donkey, if one of them rode the donkey. There was only one thing left to do.

Slowly they hoisted the donkey on to their backs and continued on their way.

No Room!

There was once a poor tailor called Jacob. He was so poor that he lived with his wife and his five children in a tiny house which only had two rooms. The children all slept together in one bed in the only bedroom, and he and his wife slept on a mattress on the kitchen floor. Because there were so many children his wife, Sarah, had to wash every day, and every morning when she swept the floor, however careful she was, she kept tripping over all the shoes and the children.

Just before the festival of Passover, Jacob climbed up a ladder and handed down the special pots and dishes, which for the rest of the year were kept in the rafters. Now the room seemed more crowded than ever. Sarah could stand it no longer. In desperation she threw down her broom. "Do something!" she cried. "We cannot celebrate Passover in this small house."

But Jacob did not know what to do. Through the window he saw the Rabbi walking down the street. Quickly he ran outside.

"Rabbi, Rabbi, what can I do? My wife says we cannot celebrate Passover for our house is too small."

The Rabbi stroked his beard and looked thoughtful; then he smiled. "You have two goats. Take them into the kitchen."

The tailor opened his mouth to protest at this silly idea, but the Rabbi had walked on. Jacob caught the goats and led them into the house. Immediately they climbed on to the furniture, jumped on the beds and began to eat everything in sight. Sarah chased her husband out of the house with her broom. He ran to find the Rabbi.

"Now our house is even smaller – what shall I do?"

The Rabbi smiled, "You have a rooster, eight chickens and four geese. Take them into your kitchen."

Again the tailor opened his mouth to protest but again the Rabbi had walked on. Jacob caught the rooster and the eight chickens and the four geese and led them into the house. They perched on the clothes lines, they crowed and clucked so loudly that no one could hear themselves speak, and the chickens laid eggs in the tailor's hat and boots. Again Sarah chased her husband from the house. Again he ran to find the Rabbi.

"The house is fuller than ever, what shall I do?"

The Rabbi stroked his beard. "Shoo the goats and the rooster and the chickens and the geese out into the yard."

Jacob and Sarah did as the Rabbi said, then rushed back into the house and shut the door. They sat down and looked around. Sarah jumped up with joy.

"The Rabbi can work miracles!" she cried. "See how much larger the house has become. It is big enough for us all to celebrate Passover in, and it is even big enough for us to invite others to share our meal."

Three Wishes

A traditional European story

Once upon a time a poor fisherman was out in his boat fishing. He had caught nothing all day, and was dreading going home to his wife with no fish for supper. Suddenly just as he was about to give up in despair, his net felt very heavy. He tugged and tugged and hauled the net into the boat. There, caught in the net, was the biggest fish he had ever seen. Just as he thought that he could now go home and have his supper, the fish spoke to him. The fisherman was astonished: he had never come across a talking fish before.

"Please let me go", said the fish.

"If I let you go, I'll have no supper", said the fisherman.

"Oh, that's all right", said the fish. "If you let me go, I can give you three wishes. With those three wishes you can have anything you want. Surely that's much better than having a poor fish for supper?" The fisherman thought about it for a while, but at last he agreed to let the fish go.

When he got home, he told his wife the wonderful news.

"Oh!" she cried. "What riches we shall have! We shall have a new house and servants, and enough food every day and I shall have a dress of finest silk and little gold slippers."

"Well," said her husband, "that's all very well, but I am hungry; I haven't had any supper and I have been out fishing all day. You know I wish I had a sausage as long as my arm." At once a sausage appeared – a fine shining sausage as long as his arm.

His wife was furious. "You old fool! Just look what you have done. You have wasted one of our precious wishes on this worthless sausage. You good for nothing dunderhead! You and your sausages! I wish your vile sausage were stuck on the end of your nose."

Lo and behold, no sooner had she spoken than the terrible deed was done. The sausage was well and truly stuck on her husband's nose! What was she to do?

She tugged and tugged at the sausage, but all she managed to do was to was make her husband cry out in pain. "My poor husband!" she said. "You may be an old fool, but how can I bear you to have a sausage on your nose for the rest of your life? I wish the sausage were as far away from here as ever could be."

At that the sausage flew out of the window, up into the sky and away into the distance. And with the sausage went their dreams of the new house, the servants, the good food, the silk dress and even the little gold slippers. They were as poor as ever, with nothing to show for their three wishes – not even a sausage for their supper!

Note:
This story can be told in conjunction with work on 'Bringing in the good luck', in the *Infant Teacher's Handbook*, page 65.

The Sun and the North Wind

A traditional European story

June 2003

KS1 Child in coat

T he Sun and the North Wind were having an argument one day.

"I am stronger than you!" said the Sun.

"No, I am stronger than you!" said the North Wind. "I can roar and puff. I can blow down trees and houses. I can make waves in the sea like mountains. I can wreck ships and make people cower in fear."

"I warm the whole earth", said the Sun. "I make the plants grow and I make the fruit ripen. I can scorch the earth dry if I choose. I melt the ice of winter, and I give light to all."

"I still say I am the stronger", said the North Wind. "I'll tell you what – let's have a contest to prove who is the strongest. Do you see that man down there, with his coat wrapped round him? Whichever of us can get that coat off him is the strongest."

KS1 Hide a child

The Sun agreed, and said that the North Wind could go first. "I will hide behind this cloud and watch you", he said.

So the Sun hid behind a cloud, and the North Wind puffed out his cheeks and began to blow. The coat flapped round the man's legs, and he pulled it closer round him. The North Wind blew and blew as hard as he could, but the harder he blew, the closer the man held his coat round him. The North Wind gave a mighty roar, and the trees bent and broke before him. The man could hardly stand up, and he turned his back to the wind to escape the blast. But still he clutched his coat tightly round him.

The North Wind sat back, tired out. "I give up", he said. "No one can get that coat off him."

"I can", said the Sun. "Just watch!"

And he came out from behind the cloud, and began to shine on the man down below them. At once the man turned round, smiled, and looked up gratefully at the sun. He stopped holding his coat round him, and began to walk happily on his way.

"Well, aren't you going to try grabbing it off him?" asked the North Wind.

"There's no need for that", said the Sun. "Just watch."

And he shone and shone as brightly as he could on the man below. For a while the man walked along happily, glad that the fierce wind had gone. But little by little he began to be uncomfortable. He slowed down, opened his coat wider, and wiped the sweat off his face. Still the Sun shone. The man grew hotter and hotter, and more and more uncomfortable. Finally he stopped, looked up at the Sun in the sky, and took his coat off

Ahera and the Dragon

A story from the Luhya people of East Africa

One day three girls went out to collect firewood to take home for their cooking fires. Two of them were good friends, but these two did not really like the third one, whose name was Ahera. When they had all collected enough wood to take home, they looked around to see what else they could do in the forest, for they did not want to go straight home.

"I know", said one. "Let's climb the trees and pick fruit."

"All right," said the other, "but let's make it more interesting. Let's all close our eyes, and pick the fruit with our eyes shut. Then when we open our eyes, we can see who has picked the most ripe fruit."

The girls all agreed to do this. But behind Ahera's back, the other two made secret signals to each other that they would not close their eyes, and play a trick on Ahera. So while Ahera was picking unripe fruits along with the ripe ones, because she could not tell the difference with her eyes shut, the other two were picking only the ripe ones, because they could see them. So when the three girls had had enough, and climbed down from the trees, Ahera opened her eyes and found that she had mainly unripe fruits, while her friends had plenty of ripe ones.

"Could you share some of your fruit with me?" she asked the others. "You have plenty of ripe ones."

"Of course not, Ahera", said the other two.

"Well then," said Ahera, "would you at least wait for me while I go and pick some ripe ones, and then we can go home together. I don't want to be left on my own in the forest."

"All right", said the other girls. "We'll wait for you."

But as soon as Ahera had climbed to the top of the tree, and was happily picking fruit, the two girls picked up their firewood and their fruit, and ran home through the forest without her.

"Stop, stop!" cried Ahera. "I don't know the way home!"

"Can't stop!" they shouted as they ran. "We'll put leaves along the path to show you the way. You'll be all right"

And they ran off laughing, picking leaves and dropping them on the path as they went.

But someone else had heard them. A dragon was lurking in the bushes, and saw them dropping the leaves. So after the two girls had gone, and while Ahera was still struggling to climb down from the tree and catch up with the other girls, he took the leaves, and laid a new trail. This trail led not to the village, but to the dragon's home.

Ahera came down from the tree, took her fruit and her bundle of firewood, and set off following the leaves. The leaves led her right to the dragon's door, and the dragon thought to himself,

"I've got a good meal here today!"

But then he looked at Ahera, as she puzzled over what could have gone wrong, and he saw that she was a very beautiful girl, and had a friendly face, so the dragon said to himself: "No, I won't eat her right now. I'll keep her as my child. Well, maybe not as my child – no, that would be a waste. But I'll keep her a few days and fatten her up. She's a bit bony, and would only make a mouthful. I'll feed her up, and then I can eat her."

So each day the dragon went out, caught some meat, brought it home, roasted it nicely, and fed it to Ahera.

For two weeks this went on. At first Ahera was afraid of the dragon, but after a while she began to realise that he could be outwitted. And one day, when the dragon left the house, he forgot to lock the door. And instead of staying cowering indoors, Ahera followed him. She followed him through the bush until he came to the main path that led from one village to another. And when the dragon turned right along the path, Ahera turned left. And then she ran. She ran and she ran until she met some people travelling on the path, and they took her home. How glad she was to be safe home at last!

When the dragon returned home that night, with meat for Ahera as usual, he found her gone.

"What a fool I am!" he moaned to himself. "Why did I not eat her when I first found her? Or even yesterday, when I still had the chance? Or even this morning? She was fat enough."

But of course wishes are not horses, or all beggars would be able to ride. It was no good wishing that he had done something different. The girl was gone. The dragon didn't know which made him saddest – the loss of his nice meal, or the loss of the bright, happy girl he was beginning to love. So he sat down at the door of his house, and he sang a song.

> "Ahera, Ahera, you were mine.
> I'm hungry, my Ahera.
> Why aren't you here, my Ahera?
> I could eat you up, my Ahera.
> How I would love that, my Ahera.
> Because I fed you, my Ahera.
> Nice and fat, my Ahera."

He sat at his door, and sang this song, on, and on, and on, mourning for his lost Ahera, until after a few days he died. And there ends my story.

212

The Foolish Old Man

A story from the Kikuyu people of Kenya

Once upon a time there was an old and well-respected man, an elder of his tribe, whose name was Managu. One day he went to the market, and sat down with the other elders, and they drank a little wine. And they talked together, and they drank a little more wine. They enjoyed each other's company, and they drank a little more wine. They sat and they sat, and they drank more wine, until eventually it started raining.

"It's late", said Managu to himself. "I must set off home." But the rain was heavy, and his home suddenly seemed a long way away. And to tell the truth, he had drunk quite a lot of wine.

"Where can I go to shelter?" he asked himself. "My son and his wife's family live near here. Maybe I could call on them."

But that presented a problem. For amongst the Kikuyu people it is very bad manners to call on your in-laws without a very good reason. You can't just drop in because it's raining and you don't want to walk home.

"What excuse can I give?" thought Managu. He thought and thought, but he couldn't think of a good excuse. But, as he thought, his feet were carrying him closer and closer to the house, and before he knew it, he was knocking at the door, and going into his daughter-in-law's house. So, to avoid embarrassment, he came out with the first excuse that entered his head.

"I'm hungry!" he said to his son's father-in-law. "Can you bring me a goat? I'm so hungry, I'll eat the horns and the hooves!"

Well, what could his in-laws do? A visitor had asked for a goat, and it would be wrong to refuse. So they led Managu to the seat of honour, lit a fire, and went out to kill the goat. They roasted the meat, and set it all on a gold tray, with a little sharp stick to use as a fork to eat it with. Then the elder of the house went to get ready so that he could sit with Managu, and keep him company while he ate.

Left on his own, Managu started poking at the meat with the stick.

"Did they put in the horns and the hooves?" he wondered. "I asked for them, so they ought to give me them!" He poked and poked, but he could not find the horns or the hooves.

"I'll go out to the yard where they killed the goat and cooked it", he said to himself. "I'll see if I can find the horns and the hooves there. They should have given me them!"

So he went out and began turning things over in the yard outside. Meanwhile the elder of the house had put on his best clothes and was coming back into the yard with his son, to keep his visitor company.

And as he passed the place where animals were slaughtered and prepared for cooking, he saw the shadow of something rooting around amongst the rubbish there.

"My goodness", he said to his son, "these hyenas are getting bolder and bolder. Look, there's one right in our slaughtering yard! And before it's dark, too!"

"I'll teach that animal a lesson!" said his son. And he lifted his spear, took aim and threw it at what he thought was the hyena. And of course it was no hyena, it was Managu.

"What a fool I am!" Managu shouted in his pain. "I left good meat in the house, and came out to be speared looking for horns and hooves, which are not even edible!"

Tales of Life, Death and the Underworld

Orpheus and Eurydice

A story from Ancient Greece

Orpheus, son of the god Apollo, was the most wonderful musician in the world. When he sang and played his lyre, wild animals came from far away to hear, stormy seas were calmed, trees uprooted themselves to follow him and rocks moved aside to let him pass.

All creation loved Orpheus, but Eurydice loved him most of all. She and Orpheus were married, and thought they would be happy forever. But their happiness did not last. One day Eurydice was bitten by a snake and died.

Then all the world looked dark to Orpheus, and even the nightingale's song was painful to his ears. He felt he could not go on living without Eurydice, so he decided to go down into the underworld to fetch her back.

Orpheus travelled to the rugged Caucasus mountains and there found the opening of the tunnel which leads to the underworld. Down into the tunnel he went. The way was long and dark and the air as cold as a serpent's heart, but Orpheus played his lyre to keep his spirit bold. At last, after many hours, he came to the river Styx that runs beside the land of the dead. The tall hooded figure of Charon the boatman waited silently for Orpheus to give him a gold coin. All the dead have a coin put under their tongue at their funeral to pay their ferry fare across the river Styx. None could travel across without it. Orpheus was penniless, but he played upon his lyre until a single tiny tear glistened in a corner of Charon's pale eyes, and he agreed to row Orpheus across the river.

When Orpheus reached the gates to the underworld the three heads of the guard-dog, Cerberus, growled at the scent of a living creature. But when Orpheus played, Cerberus sank to the ground, his huge heads resting on his paws as he dreamed of the days when he was a puppy playing under the sun.

Orpheus walked on until he came to the hall where Hades, the ruler of the underworld, and his queen, Persephone, sat on their thrones. Orpheus kneeled before them and played, singing of his love for Eurydice. He sang that if Eurydice could not return with him he would rather stay in the underworld too.

At the sound of Orpheus' music, Persephone felt that her own heart would break. She begged her husband to grant Orpheus his wish. Hades was also deeply moved and agreed that Orpheus could have his bride back. There was one condition. Eurydice would follow Orpheus back to the land of the living, but on no account must he look behind him during his journey to check that she was following.

Overjoyed, Orpheus thanked Hades and set off on his return journey, past the three-headed guard-dog Cerberus, across the river Styx and then up, up the steep passages toward the open sky. He could not see Eurydice, because he had agreed not look back until they were back in the land of the living. He could not hear her footfall because if he stopped to listen she too must stop. Gradually doubts began to crowd into Orpheus head. Was his beloved Eurydice really behind him or had Hades tricked him? Should he look around just once, quickly, to see? Hades would never know if he did, surely?

Ahead at the end of the long tunnel, he could see the light of the upper world like a spark of hope. But now, terrified that it was all a cruel trick, he whirled around. Even as his eyes fell upon Eurydice, she began to slip back into the darkness, her beautiful arms reaching toward him. The echoes of her voice calling his name faded into silence. Eurydice was gone for ever, and Orpheus was left to return to the world of the living alone.

Note:
This story can be told in conjunction with work on 'Crossing the river Styx' in the *Junior Teacher's Handbook*, page 28.

Baldur

A Norse tale

T he god Baldur was so beautiful that everyone who looked on him loved him. He was the favourite of the gods and was very happy and contented. But then a time came when he began to have bad dreams. These dreams seemed to say that something terrible was going to happen to him. The gods wanted to prevent this and so the goddess, Frigg, made everything on the earth, in the sky and in the water promise not to harm Baldur. Everything took the oath, from the highest thing to the smallest. Rocks and stones, birds, snakes, fish, animals, illnesses, fire – everything vowed not to harm Baldur. But Frigg had forgotten one small plant – mistletoe. Because it grows on oak trees, it is neither on the earth, nor in the air, nor in the water.

Now that Baldur could not be harmed – or so the gods thought – they had a new game with him. They stood around him and threw arrows at him, stones, all sorts of weapons, but none of them harmed him. They bounced off him without doing him any damage. The gods thought that this was a wonderful game.

Meanwhile the evil god Loki was very unhappy about this. He wanted to see Baldur harmed. He dressed himself as an old woman and went to see Frigg. He pretended that he did not know why the gods were so amused. Frigg told him about the oath everything had taken. Loki asked her for the exact words of the oath. She said that everything on earth, in the air and in the water had promised not to harm Baldur. Loki realised that Frigg had left out the mistletoe. As he went away, his heart was full of evil plans.

Now that Loki knew how to harm Baldur, he went back to where the gods were playing their game. One god was not taking part: this was the blind god, Hod. Loki asked him why he wasn't joining in the fun with the others.

Hod said, "I can't see where to throw. Besides, I don't have any weapon."

Loki replied, "I'll help you. I'll put a weapon into your hand and you can throw it. I'll guide your hand and you can join in the game with the others." When he had said this, Loki put a branch of mistletoe in Hod's hand and guided it so that the weapon hit its target.

When the mistletoe hit Baldur, it did not bounce off harmlessly like all the other weapons. Instead the god fell down dead. All the other gods were overcome with grief. They had lost their beloved Baldur.

The gods realised that there was one way they might be able to get Baldur back. If one of the gods was prepared to go down to the kingdom of Hel, the kingdom of the dead, it might be possible to rescue Baldur. The god, Hermod, who was Baldur's brother, at once volunteered. Meanwhile the other gods held a funeral serv- ice for Baldur, they put his body onto a boat and set it alight.

Hermod set off on his dark lonely journey to the underworld. At last, he arrived at the kingdom of Hel. He went straight to the palace of the goddess Hel and found his brother Baldur there with her. He pleaded with the goddess to let Baldur return to Valhalla, the home of the gods. Hel said that if everything in the world wanted Baldur to return, then she would let him go, but they must show that they wanted him to return by weeping for him. If eve- rything in the entire world wept for Baldur, then he would be allowed to leave the kingdom of Hel. But if even one single thing refused to weep then Baldur would stay in the underworld for ever.

Hermod went back to the gods and told them what the godess Hel had said. The gods sent out messengers over the whole world, asking everything to weep for Baldur. Because everyone and eve- rything loved Baldur so much, people, animals, trees, and even rocks wept. There was a great sound of sobbing over the whole world. It seemed that the gods had succeeded. Everything was weeping for Baldur, but then in a distant cave in a mountain the messengers found a giant goddess named Thokk who would not weep for Baldur. They pleaded bitterly with her, but she refused to weep. She snapped, "Baldur has never done anything for me. Let Hel keep what is hers."

So Baldur remained in the underworld for ever. Some say that Thokk was in fact Loki who disguised himself to make sure that Baldur never returned to Valhalla.

The Student and the Ants

An Ancient Chinese story

A long while ago in China there lived a very wise man. He had studied all the wisdom of the ancient masters, and pondered on it. He knew all about the movement of the stars and planets, and how they affect the lives of people on earth. He knew about the ways of the earth, wind and water, and how people must live and build and farm in harmony with them. And he knew about the secrets of the face, how a person's whole life, past, present and future, can be seen in their face by those who know how to look.

Now this wise man had a student, a humble lad who had come to him very young from his home many miles away, anxious to learn the ancient wisdom. The young man had studied with him, and watched his ways, and cared for him as a servant, for several years. He worked hard, and learnt well, and was always kind to others, and to the animals and birds that flocked round the hut where he lived with his master.

But one day the wise man looked into his student's face, and he was shocked by what he saw. "My beloved student is going to die within four weeks!" he said to himself. "What can I do? I cannot let him know what I have seen in his face."

So he called the student to him and said: "My dear boy, you have served me well and studied well for several years. It is time you had a holiday and went to visit your parents. Take as long as you need – six weeks or more – and come back when you have seen how they are getting on, and have told them all your news."

"At least", he thought to himself, "he will die happy, at home in his mother's arms."

So, hiding his grief, he waved farewell to his student as he set off on the long journey home. He settled back to studying the earth and sky and his ancient books, but his heart was heavy for the young man he would not see again. Time went by, and after four weeks, he said to himself, "He must be dead by now."

It was only a little while after this, that the old man was sitting in his hut as usual, reading his books, when he suddenly heard a familiar voice behind him. "I'm back, master. My parents are well, and they were delighted to see me, and to hear that you think I am worthy to be your student!"

The old man turned, amazed. It was true! It was his student come back! "Something wonderful must have happened!" he said. "Sit down my boy, and tell me all about your journey. Who did you meet? Did you do a great service for anyone on the way? Did you show kindness to man, woman or child?"

"No, master. I met no one on the way, the roads were deserted. I would have helped anyone I met if they needed it, but there was no one."

"Was there nothing unusual on your journey?"

"Well, there was one little thing. I sat down by a river one day to rest and eat, and it had been raining hard. The level of the river had risen, and I saw that a little hump in the ground had been surrounded by water, and turned into a tiny island, just a little way from the bank. On this island there was a colony of ants. They were frantic, because they couldn't reach the shore, and they were running about here, there and everywhere."

"What did you do?"

"I took a long blade of grass and put it across the water from the island to the bank, so that the ants could walk across it to safety."

"Now I understand! You have found favour with heaven! I can tell you now that I saw in your face that you were to die. But your kindness to the tiny creatures, the ants, has earned you your life. Heaven is always pleased with anyone who shows kindness to other creatures."

Alexander and Beucephalos

Alexander, son of the great king Philip of Macedonia, wandered into the great courtyard of his father's palace. The whole place was in an uproar. Grooms shouted, women screamed, tables were overturned, and mothers pulled their children to safety. And in the middle of this scene of chaos, a magnificent horse plunged and reared and lashed out with its hooves.

"Here, you!" cried Alexander, stopping a groom who was rushing by with a coil of rope. "What's going on? What's the matter with that horse?"

"It's the king's new horse, young master" replied the groom. "Paid a fortune for him, he did, and now look at him! Magnificent beast, but we can't do anything with him! He's wild, and none of us can get near him! Can't hold him, let alone ride him! We'll have to kill the creature if this carries on. Look at the king's face!"

And Alexander could see on the face of his watching father that the hard decision was going to be made. King Philip would not keep a useless horse, no matter what he had paid for it.

"No, father!" shouted Alexander. "Don't kill the horse! Let me try to get near it!"

And before his father or anyone else could move to stop him running into such danger, the boy had seized the rope fastened to the horse's head, and, very gently, turned the horse round. And as soon as he did so, the horse's mad rearing and kicking began to get less, and gradually the beautiful creature began to calm down. Slowly, slowly, Alexander moved closer and closer to the trembling animal, until he stood right beside its ear. Softly and calmly he began to speak to the horse, soothing it and stroking its head, until the horse dropped its nose into his palm and nuzzled it calmly. What Alexander had seen, and no one else had, was that the horse was not wild, but simply frightened of its own shadow. By turning it round he had moved it away from seeing its own plunging and kicking shadow, and the horse had calmed down.

And then, to the astonishment of all in that great courtyard, he leapt onto the back of the horse. The horse tossed its head and reared up, but Alexander kept his seat.

"Open the gates!" he shouted, and the groom obeyed as if in a daze. Alexander and the horse galloped out of the courtyard and away into the distance, leaving the grooms and his father gazing after him with open mouths. They were seen no more for the rest of that day. King Philip, his father, terrified for the boy's life, sent horsemen out to chase after him, but although they rode as fast as they could, Alexander and his horse had disappeared from sight.

But that night, when everyone had given up hope of finding the boy alive, there came a great hammering on the outer door of the palace. There, covered in dust and sweat, stood Alexander and the great horse. The horse was exhausted, its sides heaving and its head hanging down, but from that day on, Alexander and the horse were inseparable. Alexander called the horse Beucephalos, because there was a white mark on its forehead that was the shape of a bull's head, and that is what the name means in Greek – 'Bull's Head'.

As Alexander grew into manhood, he never went anywhere without his horse Beucephalos. They rode into jousts together. When Alexander went into exile, Beucephalos went with him. And when he became king, and set out to conquer the east, it was on Beucephalos that he rode out of the great city of Macedon, and into the history books.

In battle after battle, it was Beucephalos that Alexander rode. Horse and rider received many wounds, and when they healed, the scars gave them both a rough, battle-scarred appearance. It was on Beucephalos that Alexander rode in triumph into Babylon, and on Beucephalos that he struggled across the snowy passes of Afghanistan. And it was on a river on the border of what is now Afghanistan and Pakistan, that Beucephalos gave the greatest and final service to the master he loved.

The battle against the Indian kings was fierce and savage, and the spear thrusts came thick and fast around Alexander and his horse. In the midst of the battle, a spear thrust came that was aimed directly at Alexander's heart. Beucephalos reared up to save his master, and took the spear full in his chest, and fell to the ground, throwing Alexander to one side, but saving his life.

At once, the battle became a distant and unimportant thing for Alexander. He threw himself on the neck of the horse. Desperately, he pulled the spear out, and with his own cloak he tried to staunch the blood which poured from the wound. Around him and above him, his guards and heroes fought to protect their king, but Alexander had eyes for nothing but Beucephalos. And when the battle was won, and the Indian kings scattered, Alexander still stayed there, cradling the head of his dying horse in his arms. His soldiers brought a tent, and placed it over him and Beucephalos, but Alexander did not move. Darkness fell, and still the great horse fought for life in his master's arms. But in the darkest hour of the night, just before the dawn, Beucephalos died.

For three days, Alexander would not move from the tent. He was inconsolable. He wept, he mourned, and he held his dead friend in his arms. And it was only when the horse had to be taken out to be buried, that Alexander allowed himself to be parted from him. But even then, to mark the passing of his greatest friend, Alexander built a great city, called Beucephalon, and in the centre of the city he built a huge tomb for his horse. And having offered gifts for the spirit of Beucephalos, he journeyed on, knowing that no horse could ever take the place of this one, that he had tamed, and loved, and who had died for him.

And although the city has long since been washed away by the meanderings of the rivers of the Punjab, the memory of Beucephalos lives on.

Note:
This story can be told in conjunction with the work on 'Death of a pet' in the *Infant Teacher's Handbook*, page 46.

Alphabetic List of Stories